Slim Cuisine: Italian Style

Also by Sue Kreitzman

Cambridge Slim Cuisine
Cambridge Slim Cuisine: A Second Helping
The Complete Slim Cuisine
The Cambridge Slim Cuisine Diet
Slim Cuisine: Indulgent Desserts

SUE KREITZMAN

Slim Cuisine: Italian Style

BANTAM PRESS

LONDON · NEW YORK · TORONTO · SYDNEY · AUCKLAND

TRANSWORLD PUBLISHERS LTD
61-63 Uxbridge Road, London W5 5SA

TRANSWORLD PUBLISHERS (AUSTRALIA) PTY LTD
15-23 Helles Avenue, Moorebank, NSW 2170

TRANSWORLD PUBLISHERS (NZ) LTD
3 William Pickering Drive,
Albany, Auckland

Published 1992 by Bantam Press
a division of Transworld Publishers Ltd
Copyright © Sue Kreitzman 1992

Photographs by Sue Atkinson
Pottery from Ceramica Blue, London
Glassware from Verandah

A catalogue record for this book
is available from the British Library

ISBN hardcover 0593 021932
trade paperback 0593 021940

Typeset in 11/12 Palatino by
Falcon Graphic Art Ltd.
Wallington, England.

Printed in Great Britain by
Mackays of Chatham PLC, Chatham, Kent.

For Paul Masselli – in memory of that fateful day in 1974, when the Sausage Man and the Cook met at Sidney's backdoor.

Contents

Acknowledgements

I am grateful to Dr Alan Howard, and The Howard Foundation for their support of my research, and to my husband, Dr Stephen Kreitzman, for his support and direction of the scientific side of my work, and for his excellent suggestions about olives. Steve also introduced me to my first pizza in 1955, and has loved me to pieces for almost forty years. Who could ask for anything more?

Photographer Sue Atkinson, with the help of Carol Handslip, has captured the glory of *Slim Cuisine: Italian Style*. Her photographs illustrate exactly the vibrancy and colour of the recipes – one can almost taste and smell them on the page!

Lizzie Laczynska and Bipin Patel have designed a lovely book; Broo Doherty has – as always – been a delight to work with; Helenka Fuglewicz continues to work wonders; and editor Ursula Mackenzie has been just as calm, collected and comforting as usual.

My son Shawm has been an apt pupil. When I stand in his tiny kitchen watching him fling five cloves of garlic and a handful of chillies into his tomato-sauce infusion, I *know* that I brought him up right!

Snakehall Farm in Reach has – in season – been a bountiful source of courgette blossoms, purple Italian climbing beans, fresh herbs, garlic, tomatoes of ineffable flavour, and much more – they make the fens feel positive Mediterranean.

The Kent family have been wonderfully supportive, and the

girls – Lucy, Emma and Sarah (not to mention mother, Val) – have designed some perfectly gorgeous Slim Cuisine recipes of their own.

Mandy Moreton at BBC Radio Cambridgeshire has reintroduced me to the fun of regular radio work, and has been heartwarmingly supportive of my work.

My agent, David Grossman, has been a joy to work with, and his family – Annick and Richard – are a joy to know (and to feed!).

And my staff, Sandie Mitchel-King and Rosemarie Espley, with the help of Brenda Huebler and Mary Hardy, have continued to make my working days a pleasure.

Heartfelt thanks to all of you!

Introduction

Why is losing weight and maintaining a hard-won weight loss so difficult? The answer is all too obvious. The overwhelming problem with diets (and with weight maintenance schemes), is that the food is so *boring*. 'Real' food is so seductive, so comforting and delicious, so restorative and interesting and sensually fulfilling: how *can* we give it up for any length of time, even for so worthy a cause as weight reduction, weight maintenance and general good health? It's a knotty problem indeed, but it is one that I — as an FFF (formerly fat foodie) — am determined to unknot.

I consider myself a sort of female, culinary Don Quixote, tilting at centuries of gastronomic tradition. I'm determined to reinvent cuisine, repeal all the kitchen laws of fat dependency and establish a new set of techniques that do not depend on fat and oils, yet produce delicious food, the sort that you will *love* to eat. Arrogance, you say? Sure. But it is this arrogance that has enabled me to maintain a six stone weight loss for ten years, yet eat well — and lavishly — every day of my life. Food is meant to nourish us physically *and* emotionally, it's *meant* to be lavish, sumptuous and seductive. Slim Cuisine aims to give you just that sort of food, yet it will *not* make you fat. When food tastes this good, the urge to 'cheat' disappears. Why should you cheat? Slim Cuisine tastes so good that cravings for unhealthy food simply disappear. In fact 'normal' (i.e. high-fat) food will taste woefully

1

greasy when your palate becomes accustomed to Slim Cuisine. In my previous books I've given you all manner of goodies, including Indulgent Desserts. Let's continue the exploration of low-fat culinary possibilities. It's time to think Italian.

Slim Cuisine, Italian Style

'Italians do not regard food merely as fuel. They regard it as medicine for the soul, one of life's abiding pleasures.'

Barbara Grizzuti Harrison, *Italian Days*

Do you fall asleep dreaming of steaming platters of pasta; succulent fennel-flecked sausages; mounds of golden polenta; trays of fragrant lasagne oozing melting cheese and rich sauces? Does the very language of Italian gastronomy set your heart singing? Arrabbiatta – amaretti – risotto – ravioli; polenta – polpettine – pizza – pomodori; polpettoni – pesto – pasta – rigatoni . . . It makes a kind of culinary mantra that calms the most desperate collywobbles and brightens the deepest doldrums.

If you crave a total gastronomic Italian experience, but fear the resulting flab; if Italian indulgence is only an occasional treat, in between austere slimming meals of steamed fish, limp lettuce leaves and dry toast; then take heart! As the patron saint of all food lovers who must balance their passion for food with their passion for good health and slimness, I am here to see that you get plenty of what you crave. Indulge without fear. Nourish yourself physically, emotionally, and gastronomically. Welcome to *Slim Cuisine, Italian Style*.

Italian food is a rich panorama of regional cookery. As with most of the world, the two main regions of Italy are divided gastronomically by the type of fat used. The cuisine of the northern part of Italy is butter based – although olive oil is used, butter is the major cooking fat. Tuscany, in the north, seems to use butter *and* oil in almost equal emphasis (although Tuscan food never tastes excessively fatty or oily). Southern Italy employs an olive oil based cuisine and the taste of that fragrant oil, rather than butter, characterizes its dishes. Lard is also used in parts of the south.

Beyond these very general fat-based divisions, more specific variations define specific regions. In parts of the south, Greek influences are apparent, in Sicily, echoes of the Arabic conquest resonate in various traditional recipes. All through the country

2

(as in all of the world), each region's cuisine reflects its history, geography, climate and agriculture.

My personal Italian tradition reflects my origins: I was born in New York City more than fifty years ago. At that time, Little Italy, parts of Greenwich Village and the Arthur Avenue area of the Bronx were hot beds of Southern Italy. The bakeries, the groceries, the butchers, the cheese shops, the pizzerie, the trattorie: all overflowed with the bounty of Naples and Sicily. It wasn't until I was in my teens, and awakened to the joy, comfort and excitement of good food (my mother was a dreadful cook – it took me a while to learn that there was an outside world, gastronomically speaking), that the impact of all that New York Italian exuberance really hit me. Pizza! Tomato sauce, pasta, fennel sausages, mozzarella cheese! *Garlic!* I loved it from my first introduction to it and I still love it. The robust, exhilarating, down-to-earth peasant cookery of Naples never lets me down. As I grew older, as I began to travel and to meet people from other regions of Italy, my appreciation of the regional cuisines began to develop, but still, when I crave comfort, when I want total, uncomplicated delight, give me a pizza, a bowl of pasta with a rough, garlicky honest tomato sauce, or – best of all – give me a fennel-sausage and pepper sandwich. But give it to me Slim Cuisine-style please. Food that *fattens* can never be a true comfort.

Cooking Italian: the Slim Cuisine Way

'Stay off rich, fatty foods . . . I cook with no oil at all – even with pasta, which is difficult for an Italian.'

Sophia Loren, quoted in the *Sunday Express* magazine

Olive Oil and Olives

The basic premise of Slim Cuisine is that *no added fat* (that includes fats *and* oils) is ever used. How can one prepare Italian food without it, especially without *olive oil*? I believe very strongly that, for both health and weight reasons, processed fats and oils are a disaster. That includes margarine as well as butter (margarine is just as fattening as butter, and has health problems of its own) and it includes olive oil. I am in no way advocating a *no*-fat diet, simply a prudent *low*-fat one. Essential fatty acids are just that: essential, and therefore a certain amount of fat is necessary to the body's functioning. But these fats are available in a plentiful, fresh diet: whole grains, fruits, vegetables, lean meat, poultry and fish. I believe in getting essential fat from whole food stuffs. If you get your fat from blocks of butter, tubs of margarine, bottles of oil, you get too much of it. At 120 Calories per tablespoon, fat (and oil) adds up pretty quickly. And those Calories are metabolized in a way that will make you fatter faster (and more efficiently) than protein or carbohydrate Calories will. So forget olive oil – you should never even have it in the house. It's too easy to pick up the bottle and splash the oil around. A bit in the frying pan, a bit more on your salad – a sprinkling on your pizza, another on your pasta – before long you are swamped with the stuff.

Obtain your Italian flavour right from the source: from olives themselves. 14 grams of black olive flesh (the amount you will get from 4 whole olives) contains approximately 2 grams of fat and 19 Calories. A tablespoon of olive oil, on the other hand, contains approximately 14 grams of fat, and 120 Calories. With 4 black olives, sliced off their stones into slivers, you can make an olive-flavoured infusion that will make a lovely Italian flavour base for your Slim Cuisine Italian cookery. Only buy black olives packed in brine (not olive oil) and buy the olives that come in jars or vacuum-packed plastic. Olives in tins are inevitably flabby and tasteless.

To make an olive infusion, combine – in a non-reactive frying pan – the slivered olive flesh from 4-5 olives with a little of the olive brine, and a bit of stock (vegetable or chicken) or water, a bit of dry white vermouth (optional), some crushed garlic (as much or as little as you like), a pinch of crushed dried chillies, if you like them, and a handful of trimmed, sliced spring onion, or chopped onions. Add a few pieces of sun-dried tomato if you like. Boil, covered, for 5-7 minutes, then uncover and simmer until the onions are tender, and the liquid greatly reduced and syrupy. This infusion (and variants of it) can be used for countless low-fat yet flavourful Italian dishes. It takes about as long (and it is as easy) to make such an infusion as it takes to sauté onions and garlic in olive oil. (If you are on a weight *loss* regime, rather than maintenance, omit the olives.)

Balsamic vinegar

Balsamic vinegar is a very special vinegar produced in Modena, Italy. It is made from boiling the must of Trebbiano di Spagno grapes until it thickens and caramelizes, then culturing it in wooden barrels. The finished Balsamic vinegar – the real stuff – is very expensive, and complex and mellow enough to drink out of a glass. Many supermarkets now carry inexpensive Balsamic vinegars, factory-made rather than cottage-produced in the traditional wood-cask manner. But even these inexpensive Balsamic vinegars are very good, with a mellow, sweet taste; very useful in infusions, as well as in no-fat salad dressings. To give an olive-oil taste (without the fat) to your salad dressing, empty the brine from a jar of black olives, and replace it with balsamic vinegar. The vinegar will gradually become imbued with the olive flavour (and the olives will be beautifully influenced by the vinegar).

Sun-dried Tomatoes

Sun-dried tomatoes are like raisins made out of tomatoes rather than grapes. They are available packed in oil, or dry packed — obviously dry packed are the ones to go for (find them in speciality shops or see Mail Order Guide page 153). They are very special because they have a deep and vivid taste. 3 or 4 of them snipped with scissors and simmered in an infusion give a tremendous punch of flavour. They are not — strictly speaking — an ingredient that you *must* have: if you can't find them leave them out. It pays to seek them out, though, because they add a wonderful Italian flavour dimension to low-fat dishes. American sun-dried tomatoes are far less salty than Italian ones.

Tomatoes

Trying to find a fresh, ripe, good-tasting tomato can be a heartbreakingly futile exercise, even, unfortunately, during the summer. Hard, cottony supermarket tomatoes are no good at all — you might get more flavour out of a tennis ball! Your best bet is to try to find, in the depressing array of supermarket tomatoes, the ones that have been grown out of doors. Store them, at room temperature, in a paper bag (close a banana in with them) and leave them for a few days to a week. They will slowly ripen and develop flavour. They may not taste quite like sun-warmed, fresh-out-of-the-garden, summer beauties, but they *will* taste surprisingly good. To peel a fresh tomato, immerse it in boiling water for 10 seconds, then cut out the stem and slip off the skins. The seeds may be removed with your finger.

Dried Porcini Mushrooms

Dried porcini (*Boletus Edulus*) mushrooms are available in speciality food halls and Italian Delis (see Mail Order Guide page 153). You only need to reconstitute ½-1 ounce (10-25 grams) at a time: the results are powerfully flavourful bits of mushroom, and the gorgeous soaking liquid as well — liquid that is dark and vivid with wild mushroom taste. Always reconstitute the mushrooms in plenty of water – then, after filtering it, freeze some of the liquid to use in subsequent stews, soups, sauces and flavour infusions. It can even be used in bread baking (page 122). Always rinse the dried mushrooms first in cold water to wash away the grit and dirt, then soak in plenty of warm water for 15-30 minutes. Finally, strain through a coffee filter, and rinse the mushrooms once more. Both the mushrooms and the soaking liquid are now ready for use.

Wine and Spirits

I like to use small amounts of wine and spirits in various dishes. When boiled, alcohol evaporates, therefore the alcohol Calories evaporate as well but the good flavour remains. Dry vermouth, sherry and Marsala are fortified wines: once opened, they will keep for a while. But dry red and white wine will not keep once opened. If you use 4 fluid ounces (110 ml) of wine (or even just a splash) in a recipe and want to prevent the rest from spoiling until you need it again, try one of these methods:

1 It may sound odd, but wine can be frozen in small quantities (use small plastic tubs, or even ice cube trays or bags) and then thawed when needed for a recipe. When thawed, red wine throws a sediment, so strain it through a nylon tea strainer into the pot. There will be no loss of quality.
2 When you have used part of a bottle, decant the wine into a smaller vessel and close tightly. Air is the enemy of wine: if the wine fills the bottle or jar so that there is no air, it will not spoil.
3 You can buy a convenient vacuum gadget in many houseware departments that reseals partially empty wine bottles by pumping air out of the bottle. They cost only a few pounds, and are very easy to use.

Stock

As I have already mentioned, many of the recipes in this book begin with a flavourful infusion: a mixture of garlic, diced sun-dried tomatoes if you have them, some black olive slivers, sliced spring onions, and a pinch of dried chillies simmered in stock until the garlic, tomatoes and onions are tender (the garlic will be exquisitely *mild* as well as tender), and the mixture is syrupy. This garlic-olive infusion (or variations of it) takes the place of that Fat Cuisine staple – onions and garlic sautéed in butter or oil. What kind of stock to use? Home-made chicken or vegetable stocks are great, but I have learned that the old-fashioned ritual of saving scraps and carcasses for the stockpot, and then − periodically − cooking up a big batch of stock for the freezer, is the last thing most people want to do. Fortunately, there are plenty of options.

1   Friggs Vegetal: the label on this vegetable bouillon powder indicates that it is meant to be used as a hot vegetable drink, but it makes a wonderful vegetable stock for cooking. It is not even necessary to reconstitute the powder first; simply combine the flavour ingredients (onions, garlic, etc.) in a frying pan, add water, and sprinkle in a pinch or two of Vegetal. If you can't find Friggs Vegetal in the supermarket or health food shop (distribution tends to be spotty), it is available through mail order (see Mail Order Guide, page 153).

2   There are other low-fat, low-salt stock powders and cubes available − check out your local health food store. Always read the fine print to make sure you are buying one that really *is* low in fat and salt − then try them out and see which pleases you.

3   A company called Jürgen Langbein makes good quality, low-salt, fat-free stocks, available in jars: chicken, vegetable, beef and fish. Many supermarkets stock them.

4   If you are out of both jarred stock and bouillon powder you can substitute a mixture of water and dry white wine or dry white vermouth for the stock. Because you boil the liquid right down, the alcohol (and the alcohol Calories) evaporates, leaving the dish safe for teetotallers and children.

Cheeses

1   **Ricotta cheese** is a traditional Italian soft whey cheese with a fairly low-fat content (9 grams of fat per 3½ ounces/100 grams of cheese). Ricotta has a delicious mild taste, and a smooth texture with just the slightest hint of graininess. Look for it − in bulk or vacuum-packed − in speciality cheese shops. Its shelf life is brief, but it can be frozen. Ricotta is exquisite in desserts (Tiramisu, for instance, page 140, or Ricotta Creams, pages 147 and 148), and it is gorgeous as the creamy layer in lasagne and other Italian gratins.

2   **Quark** is a *no*-fat, smooth and creamy curd cheese. Some supermarkets carry their own brand, labelled 'skimmed milk curd cheese'. If you can't find ricotta, or you are on a weight-*loss* diet, quark can be substituted for ricotta in any

recipe. As a general rule, I like to mix the two, half and half, in order to bring the fat levels right down.

3   **Mozzarella Cheese** is a snowy white mild cheese that melts like a dream. You will find it in most supermarkets, packaged in a liquid-filled pouch. The cheese may be labelled 'full-fat', or 'medium-fat', but, either way, it will fall into the 20% fat content category — the *lower* end of full-fat as defined by government guidelines. If you are not on a weight-loss diet, a little bit of mozzarella can be used here and there in your Italian recipes. Here is some good news: you can turn mozzarella cheese into an almost *no*-fat cheese, and so use it even if you are on a weight-loss diet, or use it more lavishly when you are maintaining. Drain the packing liquid from the cheese. Put the lump of cheese into a non-stick frying pan and heat gently until the pan is filled with a mass of liquid and gooey melted cheese (oh! it will smell lovely). Pour the whole hot, sloppy mixture into a bowl or jug and refrigerate. When cooled, pour off the liquid. You will be left with an a much lower fat mozzarella cheese.

4   **Parmesan Cheese** is a medium-fat, classic Italian grating cheese with a deep cheesy taste. A little bit of Parmesan goes a very long way. One tablespoon of this medium-fat cheese adds approximately 25 Calories (1.8 grams of fat) to a recipe. If possible, buy real Italian Parmigiano Reggiano and grate it yourself as follows:
Cut the cheese into smallish chunks. Put them in the liquidizer. Blend until finely grated. Store in the refrigerator or the freezer. *Save the rind*: Parmesan rind is one of the magic ingredients of Italian cookery. Use a piece of it when simmering sauces and soups. When the dish is finished, discard the rind (or feed it to the dog). It will have imparted a good Parmesan flavour, but very little in the way of Calories or fat.

Kitchen Sense

A Note on Calorie Counts

There is nothing more boring or self-defeating than doggedly counting Calories. It can lead to a fear of food, periods of too-rigorous dieting interspersed with destructive bingeing, and the loss of any culinary enjoyment or spontaneity.

If you follow the Slim Cuisine philosophy of eliminating added fats and fatty foods, you will never have to resort to the tedium of Calorie counting. If you eliminate the fat, the Calories take care of themselves. Food is meant to be eaten with pleasure, to give us joy, keep us healthy, and provide comfort. Obsessively totalling up the Calories of everything you eat can spoil all of that.

A Note on Portion Sizes

How many people will a particular recipe serve? How can I answer that? How hungry are you and the people you plan to feed? Are you a nibbler, a grazer, a gorger or a picker? When (and what) was your last meal or snack? Because I do not have the answers to these vital questions, I am giving you plenty of leeway as far as portion size is concerned. One person's portion is another person's tantalizing tease and yet another person's over-indulgence. It is Slim Cuisine policy to allow you the freedom to decide for yourself what constitutes a portion according to the occasion and the diners. That is why, whenever possible, the yield is given in volume (for instance, 1½ pints) or in pieces (4 chicken thighs). Because the fat density is so drastically diminished, and Calorie counting is eliminated, portion control is no longer strictly necessary.

RECIPE SYMBOLS

Therapeutic Binge: There is no limit to a therapeutic binge recipe – eat all you want, as often as you like. TBs will keep you full, happy, slim and healthy. Depend on them when you are overtaken with the urge to overeat. They feed that bottomless hunger without expanding the bottom.

A recipe with a heart is *very* low in both fat and sugar. Not quite a therapeutic binge, but, still suitable for weight loss. (A recipe without a ☺, or without a ♡, is suitable for weight maintenance.) When appropriate, maintenance recipes are followed by weight-loss (♡) variations.

A clock indicates a fast recipe, perfect for those days when you come home late, there is nothing prepared in the freezer, and you want something wonderful to eat.

Snowflaked recipes can be frozen.

Any recipe that carries this symbol is suitable for vegetarians.

This symbol indicates that a microwave is needed to prepare the recipe.

9

NON-REACTIVE COOKWARE

Cast-iron, tin and aluminium cookware will react with acid ingredients, such as tomatoes, wine and spinach, to produce off-flavours and discolorations. To avoid these problems, use *non-reactive* cookware, such as enamelled cast iron, stainless steel, flame-proof glass and ceramic, and non-stick coatings such as Tefal and Silverstone. Because no added fat is used in Slim Cuisine, you will find the non-stick cookware invaluable. When choosing such equipment, go for weight. Hefty, heavy-bottomed pots and pans cook evenly and will ensure success.

How To Use These Recipes

Note: all ingredients are given in imperial and in metric measurements. Use one or the other, but do not mix measurements in any one recipe.

Before attempting to make one of these recipes, follow this procedure:
1 Read the recipe all the way through.
2 Prepare all ingredients, and measure them out. Set the prepared ingredients out on your work table.
3 Set out any equipment needed.
Then proceed with the recipe.

Soup

'But the main dish was soup, thick, beautiful, nourishing soup, such as the Italians have lived on for centuries. It was always made fresh for each meal, with none of the hocus-pocus that has come to be associated with soup making.'

Nika Standen, *Reminiscence and Ravioli*

♡ 🧸 ⏱ ❄ 🥕 **TOMATO-FENNEL SOUP**

Makes 3½ pts/2 l

Fennel, with its gentle anise flavour, combines with tomatoes to make a simple, richly textured soup. Serve it as is, or topped with croûtons (page 13) if you want some crunch to contrast with the smoothness.

1 onion, coarsely chopped	3 tins (14 oz/400 g each)
2 cloves garlic, chopped	chopped tomatoes
2½ pts/1.4 l stock	Salt and freshly ground pepper
2 heads fennel, roughly	to taste
chopped	1 piece Parmesan rind

1   Combine the onion, garlic and ½ pt/300 ml stock in a soup pot. Cover and simmer briskly, covered, for 5 minutes. Uncover and simmer until the onion is tender and the liquid gone.

11

2   Add the remaining ingredients and simmer until the fennel is tender. Remove the Parmesan rind. Cool slightly.
3   In batches, blend the soup in a liquidizer, and then push through a sieve. Serve piping hot.

❊ ⚲ PURÉED VEGETABLE-BEAN SOUP (PASSATO DI VERDURA)

Makes 3½ pts/2 l

When my husband tasted this smooth, pale green soup of puréed vegetables and beans, he looked at me quizzically. 'Are you sure this is Italian?' he asked. 'It tastes almost Jewish.' Well yes, honey, your palate has not let you down. The soup was inspired by a recipe from Edda Servi Machlin's *Classic Cooking of the Italian Jews*, now, alas, out of print. Machlin, through recipes and reminiscences, vividly recreates the Italian-Jewish community of Pitigliano, Tuscany – a community that existed from the fourteenth century until the Nazi invasion of Italy. I have substituted an olive infusion for the olive oil of the original recipe, and baked croûtons for fried croûtons. The vegetables and garlic-olive-chilli infusion give the soup its incredible flavour, the beans give it an unctuous, melting texture.

2 *cloves garlic, crushed*	*peas, leeks or spring onions*
1 *medium onion, diced*	2 *tablespoons shredded fresh*
2-3 *black olives, sliced off the*	*basil (if unavailable*
stone	*substitute some extra fresh*
¼ *teaspoon crushed dried*	*parsley)*
chillies	1 *tablespoon chopped parsley*
2½ *pts/1.4 l stock or water*	*Salt and freshly ground pepper*
2 *lb/900 g mixed vegetables,*	*to taste*
coarsely chopped: zucchini,	1 *tin (15 oz/425 g) cooked*
peeled white turnips, peeled	*cannellini beans, well drained*
carrots, potatoes, celery,	*Garlic croûtons (see below)*
trimmed green beans, green	

1   Combine the garlic, onion, olives, chillies and ½ pt/300 ml stock in a soup pot. Cover and bring to the boil. Boil for 5 minutes. Uncover and simmer until the onion is tender, and the liquid is almost gone.
2   Add all the vegetables (except the cannellini beans) and herbs. Season with salt and pepper. Cook gently, stirring for 5 minutes.

12

3   Stir in the beans and remaining stock. Simmer, covered for 35-45 minutes. Cool slightly.
4   In small batches blend the soup in the liquidizer until very smooth. Taste and adjust seasonings. Serve hot or cold, sprinkled with croûtons.

♡ Omit olives.

♡ 🥕 Croûtons
Dry slices of several day old Country Bread (page 120) in a 350°F, 180°C, Gas Mark 4 oven, turning occasionally. When they are dry and crisp right through, remove them from the oven, and rub each thoroughly with the cut side of a raw garlic clove. Cut the slices into rough ¼-½-inch/0.5-1-cm cubes.

♡ ⏱ ❄ 🥕   **SIMPLE MINESTRONE**

Makes 2½ pts/1.4 l
Minestrone (vegetable soup) can have many guises: thick and hearty, light and delicate, bursting with bits of meat, or purely vegetarian. This fresh, vegetarian version is redolent of summertime and a celebration of its ingredients.

2 medium carrots, peeled and coarsely diced	3 small courgettes, coarsely diced
12 spring onions, trimmed – the white portions diced, the green portions sliced thin	5 ripe tomatoes, skinned, seeded and quartered
3 cloves garlic, crushed	8 oz/225 g fresh or thawed frozen peas
4-5 sun-dried tomatoes, snipped (use scissors) – optional	Salt and freshly ground pepper to taste
2½ pts/1.4 l stock	3 tablespoons chopped fresh parsley
3 peppers (1 red, 1 yellow and 1 green), cored, seeded, peeled and coarsely diced	3 tablespoons shredded fresh basil or mint

1   Combine the carrots, spring onions, garlic, sun-dried tomatoes and ½ pt/300 ml of the stock in a heavy bottomed soup pan. Cover, bring to the boil and boil for 7 minutes. Uncover, reduce the heat a little and simmer briskly until the onions are tender, and the liquid is almost gone. Add the peppers and a splash of stock. Cook for a few minutes, stirring.
2   Stir in the courgettes, tomatoes and remaining stock. Simmer

13

for 10-15 minutes. Stir in the peas and simmer for 5 minutes more. Season to taste and stir in the herbs. Cook for 1-2 minutes more.

ARTICHOKE SOUP

Makes 5 pts/2.8 l

The only artichokes I seem able to find in my area are big, tough ones, with huge hairy chokes. Boiled, trimmed of their chokes and leaves, and combined with beans and pasta, they make an infinitely comforting and delicious soup/stew — a meal in itself if you serve it with a loaf of Country Bread (page 120). The leaves make a wonderful artichoke stock. I make a generous amount, because it freezes so well.

Salt	1 rounded tablespoon tomato
Juice of 1½ lemons	purée
6 artichokes	½ lb/225 g small, thin tubular
5-6 black olives in brine, sliced	pasta
off their stones	1 tin (15 oz/425 g) cannellini or
1-2 teaspoons of the olive brine	Borlotti beans, drained
3 cloves garlic, minced	9-10 mint leaves, shredded
10 spring onions, trimmed and	Salt and freshly ground pepper
sliced thin	to taste
4-5 sun-dried tomatoes, snipped	
(use scissors) — optional	

1   Bring a large, non-reactive pot of salted water to the boil. Fill a large bowl with cold water and squeeze in the juice of half a lemon.
2   Cut off the stem of each artichoke and trim the base so that it is flat. As soon as an artichoke is trimmed, immediately drop it into the bowl of acidulated water.
3   When all the artichokes are trimmed, remove each one separately from the water, snap off and discard all the tough outer leaves, and slice off the top inch of each artichoke. As each is done, return it to the acidulated water.
4   Drop the trimmed artichokes into the boiling water, base down, boil, partially covered, for 25-30 minutes. Drain (save the water) and rinse under cold water. Pull off *all* the leaves (they will pull off easily), leaving the hearts, covered by their fuzzy chokes. Return the leaves to the pot and pour in the

cooking water, topping it up if necessary. Return to the boil and simmer briskly for 15 minutes.

5   Meanwhile, trim the chokes from the artichoke hearts: with a paring knife and a teaspoon, cut and scrape away and discard all the fuzzy, hairy choke. Slice the artichoke hearts into ½-inch/1-cm thick strips.

6   Drain the leaves into a colander placed over a large bowl, pressing down, to extract all their flavour. Discard the leaves but save the water.

7   In the large pot, combine the olives, olive brine, garlic, onions, sun-dried tomatoes and ½ pt/300 ml of the artichoke water. Cover and boil for 5-7 minutes. Uncover and simmer until the onions are tender, and the liquid is greatly reduced. Add the artichoke strips, and stir and cook for a few minutes. Stir in the tomato purée.

8   Stir in 4 pints/2.3 l of the artichoke stock. Top up with water if necessary. Bring to the boil. Stir in the pasta and boil, stirring frequently, until almost tender (7-10 minutes). Stir in the beans and mint and simmer until the pasta is tender. Season with salt and pepper to taste.

♡ Omit olives.

♡ ◷ ✳ ⸙ BROAD BEAN-COURGETTE SOUP

Makes 3 pts/1.7 l

Make broad bean-courgette soup when fresh young pods of broad beans are available. Like the other vegetable soups in this chapter, this one makes the most of its collection of vegetables.

3 pts/1.7 l stock	3 stalks celery, chopped (include
10 spring onions, trimmed and	the greens)
sliced	4-5 medium courgettes, trimmed
1 ripe tomato, peeled, seeded and	and diced
chopped fine	3 tablespoons shredded fresh
12 oz/350 g shelled broad beans	basil
1 potato, peeled and cut into	3 tablespoons long-grain rice
½-inch/1-cm cubes	Salt and freshly ground pepper
	to taste
	Chopped fresh parsley

1   Combine ½ pt/300 ml stock and onions in a soup pot. Cover and bring to the boil. Boil, covered for 5 minutes. Uncover and simmer until the onions are tender and the liquid almost

gone. Stir in the tomato and simmer uncovered for 5 minutes more.

2 Add the remaining stock, beans, potato and celery. Simmer, covered for 20 minutes. Stir in the courgettes, basil and rice and season to taste. Simmer, uncovered, stirring occasionally, until the rice is tender. Stir in the parsley.

♡ ⊕ ❄ FISH STEW

Makes approx 3 pints/1.7 l

In Italian coastal areas, there are many recipes that combine tomatoes, herbs and fish. Such soup/stews overflow with a bounty of fish and shellfish. This one is severely restricted by the paltry fresh seafood pickings in most English supermarkets, nevertheless, it makes a deliciously zesty, satisfying family meal.

1 large Spanish onion, halved and sliced into thin half-moons	cod, halibut etc., cut into 1-inch/2.5 cm chunks
2-3 cloves garlic, crushed	A few well-scrubbed fresh mussels (if mussels are available in your area)
½ pt/300 ml fish, chicken or vegetable stock	
3 tablespoons Balsamic vinegar	2-3 squid, cleaned, trimmed and the body sliced into rings, the tentacles cut into pieces (optional)
¼ teaspoon crushed dried chillies (or to taste)	
1 tablespoon chopped fresh rosemary	Salt and freshly ground pepper to taste
3-4 tablespoons chopped fresh parsley	Slices of toasted Italian or French bread, rubbed with halved cloves of garlic
3 tins (14 oz/400 g each) chopped tomatoes	
1 lb/450 g mixed white fish fillets:	Additional chopped parsley for garnish

1 Combine onion, garlic, stock, vinegar and chillies in a non-reactive, heavy bottomed pan. Cover and bring to the boil. Boil for 5-7 minutes. Uncover, lower heat a bit, and simmer, until the onions are tender and the liquid is almost gone.

2 Stir in the rosemary and parsley. Stir and cook for a few minutes, stirring and scraping up any of the browned bits on the bottom of the pan. Stir in the tomatoes and simmer, uncovered, for about 15 minutes.

3 Stir in the fish, mussels and squid, and season to taste.

Simmer for 5-7 minutes until the fish is just cooked through and the mussels open. To serve, place a slice of toast in a shallow soup dish: ladle the fish and sauce over the toast. Sprinkle with parsley.

♡�֎⑂ MUSHROOM STEW, FISHERMAN'S STYLE

Makes approx 2 pts/1.1 l

Pino Luongo, in his charming book, *A Tuscan in the Kitchen*, describes the practice of — in areas away from the coast — replacing fish with mushrooms in classic tomato-fish soups/stews. What a good idea! This mushroom stew, based on an Italian fish stew, is quickly prepared, and makes a stick-to-the-ribs vegetarian main dish.

1 large Spanish onion, halved and sliced into thin half-moons	*Pinch or two crushed dried chillies (optional)*
1 lb/450 g brown cap mushrooms, halved	*3-4 tablespoons chopped fresh parsley*
2-3 cloves garlic, crushed	*3 tins (14 oz/400 g each) chopped tomatoes*
1 oz/25 g soaked dried porcini mushrooms (see page 5), chopped	*Salt and freshly ground pepper to taste*
4 fl oz/110 ml of the mushroom-soaking liquid (see page 6)	*10-12 fresh mint leaves*
½ pt/300 ml stock	*Slices of toasted Italian or French bread, rubbed with halved cloves of garlic*
3 tablespoons Balsamic vinegar	*Additional chopped parsley for garnish*
Dash of soy sauce	

1 Combine the onion, halved mushrooms, garlic, soaked mushrooms, mushroom-soaking liquid, stock, vinegar, soy sauce and chillies in a non-reactive, heavy bottomed pan. Cover and bring to the boil. Boil for 5-7 minutes. Uncover, lower heat a bit, and simmer until the onions and mushrooms are tender and the liquid is almost gone.
2 Stir in the parsley and tomatoes and some salt and pepper. Simmer, uncovered, for about 30 minutes.
3 Stir in the mint and simmer for 5 minutes more. To serve, place a slice of toast in a shallow soup dish: ladle the stew over the toast. Sprinkle with parsley.

🐻Omit bread.

Meat, Poultry and Fish

'Rather than the gift of precision a good cook needs the gift of patience, the intuition for knowing when to cover a stew and when to let a sauce boil uncovered, the knack for choosing the right pot for the right piece of meat, the curiosity to taste what's in the pot while it's cooking, the courage to correct when necessary. But over and above all of these things, one of the most important attributes of a good cook is simply the appreciation of good food.'

Wilma Pezzini, *The Tuscan Cookbook*

⏲ FETTINI (PAN-GRILLED SMALL STEAKS)

Small portions of lean meat are important to a well-balanced diet. The Italian method of quickly pan-grilling thin beefsteaks is a delicious way of having a bit of beefsteak now and then.

Freshly ground pepper	*Salt*
Lean 'Quick Grill' thin steaks	*Lemon wedges*

1   Heat a ridged grill pan until hot.
2   Sprinkle freshly ground pepper on to both sides of the steak. Place between sheets of greaseproof paper. Flatten slightly with a meat mallet. Remove the steaks from the paper.
3   Put the steaks in one layer (without touching each other) in the hot pan. Grill for 2 minutes. Lightly salt the top side. Turn and grill on the second side for approximately 2 minutes.

19

Serve with lemon wedges, or in sandwiches (page 123) with fried peppers.

✴ # BEEF IN BAROLO

Makes approx 2½ pts/1.4 l

Cubes of lean beef, combined with olives, sun-dried tomatoes, garlic infusion and a bottle of Barolo wine, and simmered in the oven for a couple of hours, fills the house with a tantalizing perfume. Serve this splendid stew with Polenta (page 101), Italian Root-Vegetable Gratin (page 72), or Potato Gnocchi (page 99).

2 onions, peeled and cut into half-moons	Pinch crushed dried chillies
4 cloves garlic, peeled and left whole	3 lbs/1.4 kg well-trimmed, point end brisket (trim off all the fat), cut into 1-inch/2.5-cm cubes
4-5 olives, sliced off the stone	
5-6 dry pack, sun-dried tomatoes, snipped (use scissors) – optional	2 tablespoons tomato purée
	1 bayleaf
1 bottle Barolo (or other dry red wine)	1 piece Parmesan rind
	Salt and freshly ground pepper to taste
5 fl oz/150 ml stock	

1   Preheat the oven to 300°F, 150°C, Gas Mark 2.
2   Put the onions, garlic, olives, sun-dried tomatoes, 5 fl oz/150 ml of the Barolo, stock and dried chillies into a non-reactive pot that can be covered. Cover and boil for 5-7 minutes. Uncover, sauté until the onions are limp and amber and the liquid is about gone.
3   Add the beef and stir over medium heat until the cubes have lost their raw redness. Stir in the tomato purée, bayleaf, Parmesan rind, salt and pepper and 1 pt/570 ml Barolo.
4   Cover and cook in the oven for two hours or more, until the meat is tender. Remove the Parmesan rind. Drain the stew into a colander over a bowl. Put the meat into a bowl and cover. Pour the juices into a jug and put into the fridge or freezer for 15-25 minutes, until the fat rises to the top. Skim off the fat and discard. Recombine meat and juices and refrigerate or freeze until serving time. Heat gently, and serve piping hot.

BRACIOLE (SMALL BEEF ROLLS)

Makes 8 rolls

When I lived in Cambridge, Massachusetts in the mid-Sixties, I learned to make beef rolls in a rich tomato sauce from Mr Tammaro, an old-fashioned Italian family butcher. I passed his shop every day on the way home from work, and, like all the Italian-Americans I have known over the years, he was always delighted to talk about recipes, techniques and food traditions. He gave me my first really good knife (he didn't actually *give* it to me, he sold it to me for a penny. 'If I *give* it to you,' he explained, 'it will cut our friendship'). These little rolls, each filled with a thin slice of Parma ham and a sage leaf, nestle in a tomato sauce that is beautifully flavoured by the beef and ham, as well as the garlic and red wine. Serve these with pasta shapes (what Mr Tammaro called 'macaroni') or Potato Gnocchi (page 99).

½ split goose skirt (see note), trimmed of any bits of fat	*½ pt/300 ml stock*
Freshly ground pepper	*¼ pt/150 ml dry red wine*
8 thin slices Parma ham, trimmed of all fat	*1 onion, halved and sliced into thin half-moons*
8 fresh sage leaves	*1 clove garlic, minced*
Approximately 2 tablespoons grated Parmesan cheese	*2 tins (14 oz/400 g each) chopped tomatoes*
	Chopped parsley

1 Slice the goose skirt, across the grain, slightly on the diagonal, into 8 slices. Place the slices on a sheet of greaseproof paper, grind on some pepper, and top with another sheet of paper. Pound with a meat mallet to flatten the slices. Remove the paper.
2 Lay a slice of Parma ham over each slice of meat, and a sage leaf over the ham. Sprinkle each with a bit of Parmesan cheese. Starting with a short edge, roll each slice into a neat bundle and tie lengthways and crossways with kitchen twine.
3 Film the bottom of a shallow, flame-proof casserole with a bit of stock and red wine (just enough to coat the bottom). Add the beef rolls and let brown on moderate heat on all sides. Remove to a plate.
4 Add the onion, garlic and remaining red wine and stock to the casserole. Bring to the boil, stirring and scraping up the browned bits with a wooden spoon. Cover and boil for 5-7

minutes. Uncover and simmer briskly until the liquid has evaporated and the onions are tender.

5   Pour in the tomatoes, and return the beef rolls to the casserole. Partially cover, and simmer for approximately 1 hour, until the meat is tender, and the gravy is thick and savoury. Serve at once (snip off the twine with scissors), garnished with chopped parsley, or cool and refrigerate or freeze for later use.

Note: When you buy the goose skirt, ask the butcher to split it horizontally into two pieces just as if he were going to butterfly it, but instead of cutting it *almost* all the way through, so that it opens like a book, he will cut it *all* the way through so that you have two pieces.

Goose Skirt Steak

Goose skirt is a cut of beef that is flat, paddle-shaped, extremely lean, and deeply flavoured — about 1-1½ lbs/450-700 g in weight. Ask your butcher if he can supply you with goose skirt. You might request that he make a habit of putting one aside for you each week. As beef cuts go, goose skirt is just about perfect. It is as lean as can be, and can be used in all sorts of interesting recipes.

BEEF ROLLANTINE

One Sunday, why not break with tradition, and have an Italian roast? This lean beef roast, stuffed with an olive and bread mixture, or the following variation, filled with Parma ham and sage, would make a welcome focus for a Sunday meal, surrounded by an array of Italian-style vegetables (see the vegetable chapter for inspiration).

½ split goose skirt (see note to previous recipe)	1 teaspoon olive brine
Freshly ground pepper to taste	2 cloves garlic, minced
10 spring onions, trimmed and thinly sliced	Pinch crushed dried chillies
	Approx. 1 pt/570 ml stock
Slivered zest of ½ lemon	1 oz/25 g dry bread, shredded
4 sun-dried tomatoes, snipped (use scissors) — optional	1 tablespoon finely chopped fresh parsley
7 black olives in brine, sliced off their stones into slivers	Juice of ½ lemon
	Approx. ½ pt/300 ml dry white vermouth

22

1 Place a piece of greaseproof paper on your work surface. Spread the meat out on the paper and sprinkle evenly with freshly ground pepper. Cover with another sheet of grease- proof paper. Pound gently with a meat mallet, or a wooden mallet, to flatten it just a bit.

2 Combine the onions, lemon zest, sun-dried tomatoes, olives, olive brine, garlic, chillies, and ½ pt/300 ml stock. Cover and boil for 5-6 minutes. Uncover and simmer until the liquid is almost gone.

3 Toss together this infusion with the bread and parsley. Moisten with a sprinkling of stock.

4 Spread this mixture on to the meat. Starting with a long edge, roll the meat into a compact sausage-like shape. With kitchen twine, tie the roll securely crossways in 3 places and length- ways. Place the roll on a platter and squeeze the juice of ½ lemon over it. Turn the meat to coat it with the juice. Let it sit at room temperature while you preheat the oven to 450°F, 230°C, Gas Mark 8.

5 Put a grill rack across a non-reactive baking dish that can also work on the hob. Pour 4 fl oz/110 ml each dry white vermouth and stock into the dish. Put the beef roll on the rack. Roast for 25-35 minutes, turning it halfway through the cooking. When the liquid in the pan has almost cooked away, replenish it with an additional splash of stock and vermouth.

6 Let the meat rest, while you place the baking dish directly on to the hob. Pour in 5-6 fl oz/150-175 ml dry white vermouth and 5-6 fl oz/150-175 ml stock. Bring to the boil. Boil, stirring and scraping up the browned bits, until you have a thick, syrupy, concentrated, powerful reduction.

7 Snip the twine from the meat and discard. With a very sharp knife, slice the meat into ½-inch/1-cm thick slices. Overlap on a serving platter. Pour the powerful pan juices over the slices.

BEEF ROLLANTINE WITH PARMA HAM AND SAGE

Fatty Italian sliced meats such as salami, cappicola and so on, are totally off limits for anyone dedicated to a low-fat diet. When this Parma ham and sage-filled roast is sliced, the beautiful pink, pinwheeled slices make a perfect substitute: they are very good in sandwiches, or as part of an antipasto platter.

½ split goose skirt (see note, page 22)
Freshly ground pepper to taste
3-4 thin slices Parma ham, trimmed of fat

4 fresh sage leaves
Juice of ½ lemon
Approximately ½ pt/300 ml stock
Approximately ½ pt/300 ml dry vermouth

1   Place a piece of greaseproof paper on your work surface. Spread the meat out on the paper and sprinkle evenly with freshly ground pepper. Cover with another sheet of greaseproof paper. Pound gently with a meat mallet, or a wooden mallet, to flatten it just a bit.
2   Lay the slices of Parma ham, in one layer, over the meat. Space the sage leaves out over the ham.
3   Starting with a long edge, roll the meat into a compact, sausage-like shape. With kitchen twine, tie the roll securely crossways in 3 places and lengthways. Place the roll on a platter and squeeze the juice of ½ lemon over it. Turn the meat to coat it with the juice. Let the meat sit at room temperature while you preheat the oven to 450°F, 230°C, Gas Mark 8.
4   Put a grill rack across a non-reactive baking dish that can also work on the hob. Pour 4 fl oz/110 ml each dry white vermouth and stock into the dish. Put the beef roll on the rack. Roast for 25-35 minutes, turning it halfway through. When the liquid in the pan has almost cooked away, replenish it with an additional splash of stock and vermouth.
5   Let the meat rest, while you place the baking dish directly on to the hob. Pour in 5-6 fl oz/150-175 ml dry white vermouth and 5-6 fl oz/150-175 ml stock. Bring to the boil. Boil, stirring and scraping up the browned bits, until you have a thick syrupy, concentrated, powerful reduction.
6   Snip the twine from the meat and discard. With a very sharp knife, slice the meat into ½-inch/1-cm thick slices. Overlap on a serving platter. Pour the powerful pan juices over the slices.

❄   **ITALIAN SHEPHERD'S PIE**

Makes a 10-inch/25.5-cm square pie

Italian shepherd's pie is a cross cultural recipe, one of the crown jewels in this collection. Rustic it may be, but it is the kind of dish I love to serve at dinner parties. The meat mixture is chilli-and-fennel-flavoured Italian sausage, simmered with tomato sauce and roasted peppers, and the topping is a golden blanket of polenta and Parmesan cheese. Bring it to the table and watch everyone beam with pleasure.

Sausage

1 lb/450 g very lean minced pork	3 garlic cloves, crushed to a
Finely chopped flesh of 3 baked	paste with a mallet
aubergines (see page 44)	4 tablespoons chopped fresh
1-2 teaspoons fennel or anise	parsley
seed	4 tablespoons dry red wine
½ teaspoon (or to taste) crushed	Salt and freshly ground pepper
dried chillies	to taste

Sauce

1 pt/570 ml Tomato Sauce (see	3 grilled peppers, coarsely diced
page 107)	(see page 46)

Polenta Topping

1¼ pt/700 ml very well-	6 tablespoons grated Parmesan
seasoned stock	cheese
6 oz/175 g quick-cooking	Salt and freshly ground pepper
polenta	to taste
4½ fl oz/135 ml buttermilk or a	Approximately 4 tablespoons
tablespoon or so of fromage	skimmed milk
frais	

1 Combine sausage ingredients in a large bowl and mix very well. Refrigerate, well covered, until needed. It can be kept, if necessary, for up to two days.
2 Put the mixture into a large heavy frying pan. Cook, stirring, over medium heat, until the meat is thoroughly cooked. Drain off fat.
3 Stir in the tomato sauce and peppers. Simmer, stirring occasionally for 15 minutes, until thick and savoury. Spread the mixture in the bottom of a 10-inch/25.5-cm square gratin dish.
4 Make the topping: heat the stock until very hot but not quite boiling. With a whisk, stir in the polenta. Switch to a wooden spoon, and stir over low heat for 5 minutes, until thick and

smooth. Thoroughly stir in the buttermilk or fromage frais and 4 tablespoons grated Parmesan cheese. Taste and adjust seasoning. It should not be bland.

5   Immediately spread the polenta evenly over the sausage base. Sprinkle with the remaining cheese. The dish may be cooled and refrigerated at this point. Bring to room temperature before continuing.

6   Preheat the oven to 350°F, 180°C, Gas Mark 4. Dribble the milk evenly over the polenta. Bake, uncovered for 45 minutes, until bubbly and brown. Let stand for 5 minutes. Cut into squares to serve.

GRILLED PORK WITH SAGE AND MOZZARELLA CHEESE

Makes 4 steaks

Pork steaks split and filled with mozzarella cheese and sage, dredged in breadcrumbs and a touch of Parmesan cheese, and grilled until golden brown . . . What luxury! Cut into the golden crust, and the cheese oozes out in a most delightful way. I far prefer this method of grilling to the traditional pan frying in butter and oil. In this version there is not a touch of greasiness, and the meat is succulent.

4 boneless loin pork steaks, 1/2-3/4-inch/1-1.5-cm thick, trimmed of all fat	Grated Parmesan cheese
	2 egg whites
	4 (1/4-inch/0.5-cm thick each)
Salt and pepper	slices mozzarella cheese, 1/4-
Plain breadcrumbs	1/2 oz/5-10 g each
	4 fresh sage leaves

1   Preheat the grill to its highest setting. Line the grill tray with foil, shiny side up. Place the rack on the tray.

2   Butterfly the pork steaks: place them flat on your work surface. Put your palm firmly on a steak. With a very sharp knife, carefully slice the steak almost through so that it opens like a book. Sprinkle the inside with salt and pepper. Repeat with the remaining steaks.

3   Combine the breadcrumbs and Parmesan cheese on a plate. Season with freshly ground pepper. Put the egg whites into a shallow bowl and beat lightly with a fork.

4   Trim the cheese slices so that they fit into the butterflied steaks. Open each steak and put a slice of mozzarella cheese

into each one. Top with a sage leaf. Close up the steaks and press the edges together. Dredge each filled steak in the crumbs, coating each side and the edges well, then dip both sides and the edges into the egg white, and dredge well again with the crumb mixture. Have a plate ready so that as each steak is ready, it can go on the plate. Refrigerate the steaks for ½-1 hour.

5   Grill the steaks 5 inches/12.5 cm from the heating element for 3 minutes on each side, until browned and crusty. Serve at once, garnished with rocket, or watercress.

❋ VEAL-GARLIC POLPETTI

Makes 25 meatballs

These little meatballs are laced with chives and garlic. If you do not share my passion for garlic, cut the amount in half, or − if you really hate the pungent bulb − leave it out. Serve the meatballs − with one of the tomato sauces in the sauce chapter − on pasta, polenta, gnocchi, or in Ballooned Sandwich Rolls (page 123).

½ lb/225 g lean minced veal	*2-3 tablespoons chopped fresh*
1 medium aubergine, baked,	* parsley*
* peeled and chopped fine (see*	*2 fl oz/50 ml dry red wine*
* page 44)*	*4 tablespoons grated Parmesan*
4 cloves garlic, crushed to a	* cheese*
* paste with a mallet*	*Salt and freshly ground pepper*
1 bunch chives, chopped fine	* to taste*

1   Preheat grill. Line grill tray with foil, shiny side up. Place the rack on the tray.

2   Combine all the ingredients in a bowl and mix very well. Fry a small piece in a tiny frying pan (no oil!) and taste. Adjust seasonings in the mixture as needed.

3   Form into 25 small balls and place them on the grill rack. Grill 3-5 inches/7.5-12.5 cm from the heat for 5 minutes. Turn and grill for 3-5 minutes on the second side. Blot on paper towels.

❋ VEAL-MUSHROOM SAUSAGE BALLS

Makes 35 balls

Salsa al Funghetto (Intense Mushroom Pâté) is a thick, deeply flavoured mushroom paste (page 115). One of my favourite ways to use the versatile mixture is to combine it with minced veal (substitute lean pork if you wish), form the veal and mushrooms into small balls, and grill gently. For a spectacular presentation, serve the intensely mushroomy sausage balls on a bed of Spicy Tomato-Apricot Sauce (page 109), surrounded by Balsamic Braised Mushrooms (page 67).

2 bunches (20) spring onions,	*1 lb/450 g lean minced veal*
trimmed and sliced thin	*1 recipe Intense Mushroom Pâté*
3 cloves garlic, crushed to a	*(Salsa al Funghetto) (see page*
paste with a mallet	*115)*
6 fl oz/175 ml stock	

1   Preheat the grill to its highest setting. Line the grill pan with foil, shiny side up. Put a rack on the grill pan.
2   Sauté the spring onions and garlic in stock in a pan until tender but not browned, and the stock is almost gone.
3   Mix the veal, Intense Mushroom Pâté and spring onion mixture together. Form into 35 balls. Grill, close to the heat, for 2 minutes on each side.

'Alice, who at our house acts as enforcer for the nutrition mob, has never had to speak on the subject of how much devastation a steady diet of Italian sausage could wreak on the human body. The limits are set. I have a sausage sandwich whenever I go to San Gennaro. I have a sausage sandwich at the Feast of St Anthony, on Sullivan Street, in the spring . . . Otherwise, I do without.'

Calvin Trillin, *Third Helpings*

❋ ITALIAN SAUSAGE BALLS

Makes 35 sausage balls

The Italian pork sausage I love beyond all others is the kind flavoured with fennel seeds and crushed dried chilli. It was this sausage that was served year after year, stuffed into crusty rolls and dripping with fried peppers, at the annual Little Italy San

Gennaro Street Festival of my youth; it was the sausage that Mr Tammaro, my Cambridge, Massachusetts teacher/butcher, produced in quantity several times a week; and it was the sausage that made my friend Paul Masselli famous. Every Saturday during Paul's reign as the Sausage Man of Atlanta, his daughter, Paula Ann, would charcoal grill pounds and pounds of the sausage in front of Sausage World, his shop/sausage plant. The sausage is, therefore, an amalgamation of Southern Italy and America. I have added a low-fat twist: the substitution of roasted aubergine pulp for pork fat. A sausage made from very lean pork mince with no added fat would be impossibly dry without the aubergine. Of course, aubergine (*melanzane*) is well loved in Italy, and prepared in countless delicious ways; why *not* roast it, and put the pulp into lean sausages?

1 lb/450 g minced lean pork	3 cloves garlic, crushed to a
2 small aubergines	paste with a mallet
(approximately 8 oz/225 g	4 tablespoons parsley, finely
each) baked, skinned and	chopped
puréed in the liquidizer (see	3 tablespoons dry red wine
page 44)	Salt and freshly ground pepper
1 teaspoon fennel or anise seeds	to taste
¼ teaspoon crushed dried	
chillies	

1 Combine all ingredients and mix very well until thoroughly amalgamated. Fry a tiny test piece (use no fat!) in a small, non-stick frying pan. Taste, then adjust seasonings in the meat mixture to your liking.
2 Preheat the grill to its highest setting.
3 With your hands, roll small balls, each a little smaller than a walnut. Line the grill pan with foil, shiny side up. Put a rack on the grill pan. Place the sausage balls on the rack.
4 When the grill is very hot, grill the sausage balls, close to the heat, for 5 minutes. Turn and grill for 2-4 minutes on the second side. Blot on paper towels to remove any trace of fat. Refrigerate until needed.

Serving Suggestions
1 Serve the Italian Sausage Balls stuffed into crisp baguettes, or Balloon Sandwich Rolls (page 123), garnished with oodles of Fried Peppers (page 65).
2 Serve on a bed of Tomato Sauce (page 107) surrounded by Balsamic Braised Mushrooms (page 67).

3   Serve with mashed potatoes, pasta or polenta.
4   Serve on a platter, on a bed of Quick Tomato Sauce with Capers (page 109). Surround with overlapped slices of Broccoli Polenta (page 104).

❄ CHEESE STUFFED MEATBALLS

Makes 30 meatballs

A tiny heart of melting mozzarella nestles in the centre of each delicate meatball.

10 oz/275 g minced beef (very lean)	1 tablespoon chopped fresh parsley
2 medium aubergines, baked, peeled and finely chopped	1 tablespoon shredded fresh basil or mint
2½ tablespoons breadcrumbs	Salt and pepper to taste
3 tablespoons grated Parmesan cheese	Approximately 2½ oz/60 g Italian mozzarella cheese

1   Line a grill pan with foil, shiny side up. Put a rack on the grill pan. Preheat the grill to its highest setting.
2   Put the minced beef in a bowl. Add the aubergine, breadcrumbs, Parmesan cheese, herbs, salt and pepper. Mix very well with a fork or your hands. In a tiny frying pan, fry a tiny test piece, without using any fat. Taste and then adjust seasonings in the mixture to your liking.
3   Cut the mozzarella cheese into 30 small pieces. Make the meatballs, enclosing a small piece of mozzarella cheese in the centre of each. Roll each meatball thoroughly between the palms to enclose the mozzarella cheese.
4   Arrange the meatballs on the grill rack. Grill for 3-5 minutes on one side, and 2-3 minutes on the second. Blot very well on paper towels.

❄ STUFFED CABBAGE ITALIAN STYLE

Makes 35 cabbage rolls

Savoury mince wrapped in cabbage leaves and braised until tender appears over and over again in the cuisines of many countries. In the Italian version, the leaves enclose pork mince and roasted aubergine pulp seasoned with garlic, fennel and red wine.

---

1 large head cabbage	4 tablespoons parsley, finely
1 lb/450 g very lean minced pork	chopped
3 small aubergines	3 tablespoons dry red wine
(approximately ¾ lb/350 g	Salt and freshly ground pepper
each), baked, skinned and	to taste
puréed in the liquidizer	10-12 spring onions, trimmed
1 teaspoon fennel or anise seeds	and sliced
¼ teaspoon crushed dried	2 heads fennel, trimmed and
chillies	diced
2-3 cloves garlic, crushed to a	½ pt/300 ml stock
paste with a mallet	2-3 fl oz/50-75 ml vermouth
	Approximately ¾ pt/400 ml
	Tomato Sauce (see page 107)

---

1   Cut the core out of the cabbage and pull off the tough outer leaves. Cook the cabbage, in enough boiling water to cover, for 5 minutes, until the cabbage leaves begin to separate and become flexible. As they separate, pull them out carefully with tongs and drain. You should end up with about 18 nice leaves. Spread the drained leaves on paper towels and cover with additional paper towels to dry well. With a small knife, pare down the tough vein on each leaf.

2   Make the stuffing: combine the pork, aubergines, fennel, dried chillies, half the garlic, parsley, red wine, salt and pepper and mix very well until thoroughly amalgamated. Fry a tiny test piece in a small non-stick frying pan. Taste, then adjust seasonings in the meat mixture to your liking.

3   Preheat the oven to 350°F, 180°C, Gas Mark 4.

4   Combine the spring onions, the remaining garlic, fennel, ½ pt/300 ml stock and the vermouth in a heavy enamelled frying pan. Cover, bring to the boil, and boil for 5 minutes. Uncover, and cook briskly until the liquid is almost gone and the vegetables are tender. In a gratin dish make a bed of this mixture.

5   Place a cabbage leaf on your work surface. Put some of the meat mixture on to the leaf. Fold over, tuck in the sides and roll neatly. Place the cabbage roll, seam side down, on the onions in the gratin dish. Repeat until all the cabbage is used. Pour the tomato sauce over and around the cabbage. Cover and cook for 1½ hours.

OSSO BUCO

Makes 6 pieces

Osso Buco means 'hollow bone'; it refers to slices of meaty veal shank with its central bone. The marrow contained in the bone is considered a great delicacy; in Italy, Osso Buco is usually served with a tiny spoon for digging out the marrow. But marrow is much too fatty for a low-fat regime; in fact, if you are accustomed to a low-fat lifestyle, you will find the fattiness of the marrow unpleasant. It's easy to dig it out from the hollow bone and discard it before cooking. The veal slices cook to melting tenderness in their bath of tomatoes and onion-garlic-olive infusion. Many traditional recipes for Osso Buco call for a last-minute sprinkling of 'Gremolada': a raw mixture of chopped garlic, grated lemon zest, and parsley, but I find it much too strong, and instead prefer to add a little lemon zest, parsley and basil during the last 10 minutes of cooking.

6 slices of veal shank, trimmed of any fat, and the marrow scraped out of the bone cavity	*1 tin (14 oz/400 g) chopped tomatoes*
1 medium onion, finely chopped	*Salt and freshly ground pepper to taste*
3 cloves garlic, chopped	*Parmesan rind*
5 olives, sliced off the stone	*Zest of one lemon*
4 sun-dried tomatoes, snipped (with scissors) — optional	*1 tablespoon fresh parsley, chopped*
½ pt/300 ml stock	*1 tablespoon fresh basil, chopped*

1 In a non-stick frying pan, brown the veal shanks on both sides. Set aside.
2 Preheat oven to 400°F, 200°C, Gas Mark 6.
3 Combine the onion, garlic, olives, sun-dried tomatoes and ½ pt/300 ml stock in a heavy non-reactive frying pan. Cover and boil for 5-7 minutes. Uncover and simmer until the onions are tender and the liquid almost gone.
4 Add the chopped tomatoes, salt, freshly ground pepper and Parmesan rind. Simmer uncovered for approximately 5 minutes.
5 Place the veal shanks in an oven-proof dish and pour the sauce over the meat.
6 Cook, covered in the oven for 30 minutes, reduce the oven temperature to 300°F, 150°C, Gas Mark 2 for a further 30 minutes. Reduce the oven temperature again to 275°F, 140°C,

Gas Mark 1 for a further 40-60 minutes.

7 Drain the juices from the meat and vegetables, and place the juices in a jug or bowl in the freezer for approximately 20-30 minutes so that the fat can rise to the top.
8 Skim the fat from the juices and discard. Re-heat the juices to liquefy them. Pour over the meat and vegetables. Cover and refrigerate until needed.
9 Pre-heat the oven to 350°F, 180°C, Gas Mark 4.
10 Heat the dish, covered, in the oven for approximately 20 minutes. Combine the lemon zest, parsley and basil, and sprinkle over the meat. Cook, covered, for approximately 10 minutes more.

VEAL MILANESE

Makes 4 pieces

Veal Milanese is one of the simplest recipes imaginable; bread-crumbed veal cutlets, quickly pan-fried in butter and oil. Here, they are grilled instead. I love them in Country Bread (page 120), lavished with grilled or fried peppers.

Approximately ½ pt/300 ml plain breadcrumbs	2 egg whites
2-3 tablespoons grated Parmesan cheese	4 veal cutlets
Freshly ground pepper	Watercress
	Lemon wedges

1 Preheat the grill to its highest setting. Line the grill tray with foil, shiny side up. Place the rack on the tray.
2 Spread the breadcrumbs and Parmesan on a plate. Season with freshly ground pepper. Put the egg whites into a shallow bowl and beat lightly with a fork.
3 Dredge each cutlet in the crumbs, coating each side and the edges well, then dip both sides and the edges into the egg white, then dredge well again with the crumb mixture. Have a plate ready so that as each cutlet is ready, it can go on the plate. Refrigerate the meat for ½-1 hour.
4 Grill the cutlets 3 inches/7.5 cm from the heating element for 1½-2 minutes on each side, until browned and crusty. Serve at once, on a watercress-garnished platter with lemon wedges or serve in crusty baguettes or Italian bread, garnished with fried peppers.

※ # STRACOTTO (MEAT FILLING)

Makes 2 pts/1.1 l meat filling

The literal meaning of Stracotto is 'overcooked'. It refers to the long, slow stewing of meat, either a large pot roast, a stew, or — as here — finely diced meat. The long cooking is mostly unattended (you just need to stir occasionally) and it fills the kitchen with the tantalizing aroma of pan-roasting meat. This stracotto can be used as a filling for Lasagne (page 98) or Cannelloni (page 92). It's one of those staples to make in quantity, and then store in the freezer until needed. Because roasted aubergine is stirred into the mixture to bulk it out, a mere 1 lb/450 g of meat yields 2 pts/1.1 l of rich tasting filling and the texture is superb.

1 lb/450 g lean pie veal or lean leg of pork cubes (or use a mixture of both)	1 pt/570 ml stock
	½ pt/300 ml dry red wine
	3 tins (14 oz/400 g each)
Chopped pulp of 3 roasted aubergines (see page 44)	chopped tomatoes
	Salt and freshly ground pepper
3 cloves garlic, crushed	to taste

1   Chop the veal or pork into fine dice. (The food processor is excellent for this. Put the meat in and pulse on and off until the meat is finely diced, *not* minced.) Put it into a heavy-bottomed, non-reactive frying pan or shallow, wide casserole with the aubergine pulp and crushed garlic. Mix it together very well. Pour in the stock and wine and bring to a simmer. Simmer, uncovered, until the liquid is almost gone, approximately ½ hour.
2   Pour in the tomatoes and season to taste. Simmer, partially covered, stirring occasionally, until the mixture is very thick (approximately one hour).

POLPETTONE

Makes 1 loaf – 9 inches/23 cm long, 5 inches/12.5 cm wide

Polpettone is Italian meat loaf, absolutely delicious served warm or cold. Cold and sliced thin, serve it on an antipasto platter in place of fatty Italian sausages such as cappicola, salami, and so on, or spread Country Bread (page 120) with Intense Mushroom Pâté (page 115) and top with a thin slice of polpettone. The meat mixture is a bit wet, loose and difficult to handle at first, so be careful when you turn it in step 4. Wear sturdy oven gloves on both hands because the dish will be very hot. When you remove the finished meat loaf from the baking dish, don't worry if a bit of it sticks to the dish.

1 batch Italian Sausage mix (see page 28)	mushroom-soaking water – page 5)
9 oz/250 g lean minced veal	2 egg whites, lightly beaten
3 slices (1 oz/25 g each) day old white bread or Country Bread (page 120)	Salt and freshly ground pepper to taste
	Dry breadcrumbs
6-8 tablespoons of stock (chicken stock, vegetable stock or	5 fl oz/150 ml dry white wine
	A few fl oz stock

1 Preheat the grill.
2 Combine the sausage mix and veal.
3 Remove the crusts from the bread. Shred the bread into a bowl and moisten with the stock; combine with a fork until the mixture forms a pap. Stir the pap and the egg white into the meat. Work it all together until it is very well combined. Fry a tiny piece in a small frying pan (use no oil!) and taste for seasonings. Add salt and pepper as needed.
4 Spread the dry breadcrumbs out on a plate and season lightly with salt and pepper. Press and form the meat into a compact oval loaf, 8-9 inches/20.5-23 cm long, 4½-5 inches/11-12.5 cm across. If it is very loose, and difficult to form into a loaf, mix in a tablespoon or so of breadcrumbs first. Roll the loaf in the crumbs on the plate, pressing them in. Put the loaf into a shallow, non-reactive baking dish. Grill until well browned on top. With 2 fish slices and extreme care, turn the loaf, and grill until well browned on the second side. Turn off the grill and set the oven at 400°F, 200°C, Gas Mark 6.
5 Pour the wine and stock around the loaf to a depth of about 1½ inches/3.5 cm. Bake, uncovered, for about 1½ hours, until the loaf is richly browned. Baste 2-3 times during the cooking. If the liquid evaporates before the loaf is done, add an extra fluid ounce/25 ml or so of stock, but when the dish is done, the liquid should be just about gone.
6 Let the loaf sit for 10-15 minutes before carefully lifting it (use 2 fish slices again) to a platter.

CHICKEN WITH PORCINI MUSHROOMS

Makes 8 pieces

Chicken is a low-fat and healthy meat, only if the skin and fat are carefully removed. Skinned chicken thighs become perfectly browned and glazed if they are first braised in liquid in a non-stick pan, then allowed to brown slowly. The finished colour is beautiful, and the taste of the braising ingredients infuses the chicken right down to the bone. Here the chicken braises with reconstituted porcini mushrooms and their soaking liquid.

8 chicken thighs, skinned (remove every vestige of skin, fat and gristle)	mushrooms, soaked, drained and chopped (see page 5)
2-3 fresh sage leaves, torn in half	Salt and freshly ground pepper to taste
1-2 sprigs fresh rosemary	8 fl oz/225 ml mushroom-soaking water
1 oz/25 g dried porcini	8 fl oz/225 ml dry white wine

1   Put the chicken thighs, skinned side down, into a heavy-bottomed, non-reactive frying pan or shallow casserole. Scatter in the herbs and mushroom pieces. Sprinkle with salt and pepper. Pour in 5 fl oz/150 ml mushroom-soaking water and 5 fl oz/150 ml wine. Bring to a simmer.

2   Simmer uncovered for 10-15 minutes turning the chicken with tongs every few minutes. Pour approximately half the pan liquid into a measuring jug or bowl and set aside. Continue simmering the chicken, turning it occasionally. After 10-15 minutes, the liquid remaining in the pan should be very thick and reduced, and the chicken almost cooked through. (If the liquid is *not* thick and reduced, remove the chicken to a plate and cover loosely with foil to keep it warm. Boil down the pan juices until they *are* thickened and reduced. Return the chicken to the pan.) Turn the heat up a bit and cook, turning the chicken frequently, until the pieces are just cooked through and richly glazed. Put the chicken on to a plate and cover loosely with foil.

3   Pour the remaining wine and mushroom liquid into the pan and bring to the boil. Boil, scraping up the browned bits in the pan, until reduced to almost a glaze. Pour in the reserved pan liquid. Boil until very thick, reduced and concentrated. Turn the chicken in the sauce to heat through. Serve at once.

PAN-BRAISED CHICKEN WITH RED VERMOUTH

Makes 4 pieces

Red vermouth has both bitter-sweetness, and herbal undertones; I think it makes an inspired cooking medium for pan-braised chicken thighs. The garlic, because it is simmered in the liquid along with the chicken, takes on a melting mellowness – there is none of the vulgar, acrid quality that sometimes comes with frying garlic in fat or oil.

4 chicken thighs, skinned and trimmed of all fat	2-3 cloves garlic, peeled and coarsely chopped
Approximately 4 fl oz/110 ml stock	Salt and freshly ground pepper to taste
Approximately 4 fl oz/110 ml red vermouth	

1 Arrange the chicken, skinned side down, in a heavy-bottomed, non-reactive frying pan. Pour in the liquid and scatter the garlic pieces around the chicken. (The chicken should be in one uncrowded layer.) Season lightly with salt and pepper. Bring to a simmer.

2 Cook uncovered, turning the chicken occasionally, for about 20 minutes. As it cooks, the liquid will reduce down considerably. When the juices are thick and syrupy, the chicken will brown nicely (turn it frequently at this point). When the chicken is meltingly tender, there is no pink at the bone, and the garlic is very tender in a thick syrupy sauce, the dish is done. If, during the cooking, the liquid cooks away, add a bit more as needed. If, on the other hand, the chicken is tender and cooked through, and there is a considerable amount of liquid left, remove the chicken to a plate, and boil the pan juices down. Then return the chicken to the sauce.

PAN-BRAISED CHICKEN WITH LEMON

Makes 4 pieces

In this variation, the chicken is braised with lemon, stock and garlic. The garlic becomes gently mellow, the lemon and stock cook down to creaminess and the vivid flavours saturate the flesh of the chicken.

4 chicken thighs, skinned and trimmed of all fat	2-3 cloves garlic, coarsely chopped
4 fl oz/100 ml stock	Salt and freshly ground pepper to taste
Strained juice of 1 large lemon	

1   Arrange the chicken, skinned side down, in a heavy-bottomed non-reactive frying pan. Pour in the stock and half the lemon juice, and scatter the garlic pieces around the chicken. (The chicken should be in one uncrowded layer.) Season lightly with salt and pepper. Bring to a simmer.

2   Cook uncovered, turning the chicken occasionally, for about 20 minutes. As it cooks, the liquid will reduce down considerably. When the juices are thick and syrupy, the chicken will brown nicely (turn it frequently at this point). Squeeze in the remaining lemon juice and cook, turning the chicken constantly, for another minute or two. If, during the cooking, the liquid cooks away, add a bit more as needed. If, on the other hand, the chicken is tender and cooked through, and there is a considerable amount of liquid left, remove the chicken to a plate, and boil the pan juices down. Then return the chicken to the sauce.

♡CHICKEN BREASTS WITH MUSHROOMS

Serves 2

If — as I suggest — you keep staples like Intense Mushroom Pâté and Tomato Sauce in the freezer at all times, elegant dishes like this are incredibly quick and easy to prepare. This recipe tells you how to serve 2 chicken breasts, but you could very easily serve 4, 6 or even 8 with one batch of the mushroom mixture. Each chicken breast is stuffed with a bit of the mushroom mixture, wrapped in a foil packet, baked in a hot oven, and served on a bed of mushrooms and tomato sauce.

2 skinless, boneless chicken breasts	Salt and freshly ground pepper to taste
Approximately 1 teaspoon dry white vermouth	Approximately 4 fl oz/110 ml warm Tomato Sauce (see page 107)
Approximately ½ pt/300 ml Intense Mushroom Pâté (see page 115)	

38

1 Preheat the oven to 450°F, 230°C, Gas Mark 8.
2 Trim any vestiges of skin, gristle and fat from each chicken breast. Pull off the loose flap of meat underneath each one. Trim and scrape the white tendon from each flap and discard the tendon. Finely dice the flap of meat.
3 Toss the diced chicken meat in a non-stick saucepan with the teaspoon vermouth, over a moderately high heat for a minute or so, until barely cooked through. Do not overcook or it will be tough. Mix it with two tablespoons of the mushroom pâté. Set aside. Warm the remaining mushroom pâté.
4 Place the chicken breasts, skinned side up, on your work surface. Place your hand flat on one of them, and − with a sharp knife − starting at the thicker edge, carefully cut partially through the breast, horizontally, so that it has a pocket. Repeat with the second chicken breast. Season the inside of the pocket with salt and pepper. Fill each pocket with a tablespoon of the mushroom-chicken mixture. Press the edges together to seal. There is no need to skewer the pocket closed; the chicken meat will adhere to itself.
5 Cut a square of aluminium foil that will enclose both filled breasts in one uncrowded layer. Lay it out on your work surface, shiny side up. Put the breasts, not touching each other and skinned side up on the bottom half of the foil. Season with salt and pepper. Fold the foil over and seal tightly all around. Place on a baking tray, and bake in the hot oven for 10 minutes. The foil bag will puff up.
6 Meanwhile, coat a warm serving plate with a thin layer of tomato sauce. Cover with a layer of mushroom sauce, but leave a border of tomato sauce visible all around. Cover loosely with foil and keep warm. After 10 minutes, unwrap the foil packets of chicken. Centre the breasts on the mushroom sauce. Pour the juices in the foil over them. Serve at once.

LEMON-ROSEMARY ROASTED CHICKEN

If you slip lemon slices, garlic and rosemary sprigs under the breast of a whole chicken, and then roast the chicken, the flesh becomes imbued with the glorious flavours of those aromatic ingredients. The pan juices, augmented with a bit of vermouth, are extraordinarily good.

1½ lemons	2 sprigs fresh rosemary
1 medium (2½-3 lb/1-1.5 kg) roasting chicken, trimmed of fat	2 cloves garlic, crushed
	4-6 fl oz/110-175 ml dry white vermouth
4 thin slices of lemon (remove pips)	

1 Squeeze the juice from the lemons. Make small incisions all over the chicken (except in the breast) and rub in the lemon juice. Loosen the breast skin. Rub beneath the skin with lemon juice. Slip the 4 lemon slices (2 on each side) under the breast skin along with the rosemary sprigs and the garlic. Place the squeezed lemon halves in the chicken's cavity. Marinate overnight in the refrigerator.

2 Next day, preheat the oven to 450°F, 230°C, Gas Mark 8. Place a rack across a flameproof shallow roasting pan. Place the chicken on the rack and roast breast down for 15 minutes, breast up for approximately 45 minutes or until just done. If the juices on the bottom of the roasting dish start to burn, pour in an ounce or two/25-50 ml vermouth. When the chicken is done, tip the juices from the cavity into the roasting pan.

3 Allow the chicken to rest on a plate, loosely covered with foil. Tilt the roasting pan, and prop it up in the tilted position. With a large spoon, spoon out all fat (there will be plenty) and discard. Put the roasting pan level on the hob, and turn the heat on full. Stir and scrape up the drippings and browned bits. Pour in 4-6 fl oz/110-175 ml dry white vermouth. Boil, stirring and scraping, until you have a dark, thick, rich sauce, and the alcohol has cooked away. Serve this sauce with the carved chicken. (Discard the skin and the lemon slices, rosemary and garlic beneath the skin.)

♡ Eat the breast meat — leave the remainder for the rest of the family.

♡ ⊕ COD WITH SPRING ONIONS AND MINT

Makes 4 pieces

Quantities of shredded fresh mint mixed with fresh parsley and sliced spring onions make a delicate, fresh-tasting bed for cod fillets. The fish should be cooked for 5 minutes per ½-inch/1-cm thickness, so measure before you bake.

10 spring onions, trimmed and sliced	¼ pt/150 ml fish stock
2 cloves garlic, crushed	4 equal-sized pieces of cod fillet
4-6 tablespoons shredded mint	Salt and freshly ground pepper to taste
4-6 tablespoons chopped parsley	Lemon wedges
Juice of ½ lemon	

1 Preheat the oven to 450°F, 230°C, Gas Mark 8.
2 Combine the spring onions (save some of the sliced green part for garnish), garlic, mint and parsley, lemon juice and stock in a baking dish that can hold the cod in one un-crowded layer.
3 Place the cod fillets on the herb-garlic mixture and turn them to moisten. Season with salt and pepper.
4 Bake in the oven for 5 minutes per ½-inch/1-cm thickness. Serve at once sprinkled with the reserved fresh spring onion greens. Serve with lemon wedges.

PIQUANT SWORDFISH

Makes 2 steaks

Swordfish steaks are thick, meaty and succulent when properly cooked. Never cook them for longer than 5 minutes per ½-inch/1-cm thickness, or they turn dry and cottony. The swordfish available in British supermarkets is frozen and – usually – thawed before being placed on display. Buy it still frozen (why buy thawed fish that has been languishing for a while?) and carry it home in a cold bag filled with a few cold blocks. Then store it in the freezer until it's time to thaw it (in the fridge, overnight) and cook it. Always smell the frozen fish before you buy. If it smells fishy, forget it. What smells fishy when frozen, will smell (and taste) even worse when it thaws. Fresh-frozen fish should have no whiff of fishiness whatsoever.

Approximately ¼ pt/150 ml Quick Tomato Sauce with Capers (see page 109)	1 tablespoon raisins
	Juice of ½ lemon
	1 teaspoon balsamic vinegar
2 swordfish steaks	Freshly ground pepper to taste

1 Preheat the oven to 450°F, 230°C, Gas Mark 8.
2 Spoon the sauce into a 9-inch/23-cm square, 2-inch/5-cm

41

deep baking dish. Place the swordfish steaks on the sauce. Scatter the raisins over the steaks, squeeze on the lemon juice and sprinkle on the vinegar. Grind on some pepper.

3   Bake uncovered for 5 minutes per ½-inch/1-cm thickness (approximately 10 minutes). Put each steak on a plate and spoon the sauce over it. Serve at once.

♡ Omit raisins.

♡
SWORDFISH MARINATED IN LEMON AND GARLIC

Makes 2 steaks

Remember, measure the fish steaks, and cook them for 5 minutes per ½-inch/1-cm thickness, or they will be dry. If you first marinate the steaks overnight in a mixture of lemon juice, vermouth, and garlic, the fish will be saturated with the gorgeous flavour.

2 swordfish steaks	*1-2 cloves garlic, minced*
Juice of 2 lemons	*Freshly ground pepper to taste*
2 tablespoons dry white vermouth	*Juice of an additional ½ lemon if necessary*

1   Put the swordfish steaks into a shallow non-reactive baking dish. Squeeze the juice of 1½ lemons over and around the fish. Sprinkle in the vermouth, scatter on the garlic, and grind on some pepper. Turn the fish a few times to coat it with the marinade. Cover the dish and refrigerate for a few hours or overnight. (Turn the fish in the marinade once or twice.)

2   Remove the dish from the refrigerator to warm it up a bit while you preheat the oven to 450°F, 230°C, Gas Mark 8. If most of the marinade has been absorbed into the fish, squeeze on the juice of another ½ lemon.

3   Bake uncovered for approximately 5 minutes per ½-inch/1-cm thickness. Serve at once.

Vegetables

'No matter what, even if the family were starving to death and a dish were made from the poorest ingredients, the peasant always added the final touch — the particular taste of aromatic herbs. And people say peasants are ignorant? I think they show great knowledge of their environment and the land they work.'

Pino Luongo, *A Tuscan In The Kitchen*

Basic Vegetable Techniques

 ### BAKED GARLIC

I grew up on Naples-inspired Italian-American cuisine, and, therefore, associated Italian cookery with lots of garlic. Eventually I learned that Italian cuisine is very regional, and that not *all* the regions of Italy glow with the kind of garlic luminosity that bathes part of the South. I love garlic, but my personal taste is for a garlic flavour that is mellow, rather than ferocious. That's why I love the Slim Cuisine garlic infusion (page 6), and that's why I love *baked* garlic. When whole garlic bulbs are wrapped in foil and baked for about an hour, they take on a luscious melting texture and a gently, mellow, unbelievably delicious taste. It's like a heavenly (flavourful but not blatant) garlic butter. It doesn't *bludgeon* the tastebuds — it caresses.

Only buy fresh, firm, heavy heads of garlic, that have no shrivelled cloves, and are not sprouting. Never refrigerate them, and never wrap them. Store the heads in a cool, ventilated place. (An uncovered basket in a cool part of the kitchen is perfect.)

The purée from a hot, freshly baked head of garlic is incomparable spread on freshly baked bread (see bread chapter) or use the purée in sauces and spreads (see Ricotta Pesto, page 116 as an example.)

Whole heads of garlic

---

1   Preheat the oven to 375°F, 190°C, Gas Mark 5.
2   Remove the papery outer covering of the whole garlic heads, but do not separate the cloves or peel them. Place each whole head of garlic on a square of foil (shiny side up). Fold up the foil and crimp so that the head is completely wrapped.
3   Bake in the preheated oven for approximately 1-1¼ hours (the timing depends on the size of the garlic bulbs). The perfume that will waft through your kitchen while the garlic bakes is simply beyond description. It is *wildly* compelling. Just try it!
4   Remove from the oven, unwrap and cool for at least 5 minutes. Gently separate the cloves and squeeze each one over a fine-meshed sieve so that the softened garlic pops into the sieve.
5   With a wooden spatula or spoon rub the garlic through the sieve into a small container or bowl. (If you are in a hurry, forget the sieve. Simply squeeze the garlic into the bowl.) Cover tightly with plastic wrap and refrigerate until the purée is needed.

 BAKED AUBERGINE

Baked aubergine is one of the staples of Slim Cuisine. Aubergine (*melanzane*) is one of the stars of Southern and Mediterranean Italian Cuisine, therefore it's tailor-made for Slim Cuisine, Italian Style. The chopped pulp of the baked aubergine replaces fat in all Slim Cuisine sausage, meatball and meat sauce recipes. I know it sounds like an odd idea, but believe me: it imparts moistness and substance to the finished dish that would be sadly lacking if the aubergine were missing. Sauces, sausages and meatballs made from very lean meat would be as dry as dust, 'bitty' and boring without the aubergine. And it stretches the meat, so that you eat much less of it, yet the final texture is very meaty.

1   Preheat the oven to 400°F, 200°C, Gas Mark 6.
2   Pierce the aubergines in several places with a fork or thin
    skewer. Bake directly on the oven rack for 30-40 minutes,
    until soft and collapsed. Cool.
3   Cut away the stem, strip off and discard the skins, then chop
    finely or mash the flesh. (If the clumps of seeds are large and
    tough they may be discarded.)

 BAKED BEETROOT

Fresh beetroot is a gem of a vegetable. The colour, of course, is
dazzling: I love all shades of red, and beetroot (and its juices)
radiate a satisfyingly scarlet glow. (In fact, the vivid redness of
beetroot made people believe, long ago, that it strengthened the
blood.) But beetroot's earthy taste is satisfying, too, as well as its
supple texture, when baked and sliced. I wouldn't say that
beetroot is one of the most typical of Italian vegetables, although
they do turn up here and there in salads. But a most intriguing
Italian beetroot recipe appears in Waverly Root's *The Best of
Italian Cooking*. He describes *Barbabietole alla Parmigiana*: slices of
cooked beetroot layered with meat sauce and grated Parmesan
cheese — very like lasagne, with beetroot slices standing in for
the lasagne sheets. It is a beautiful and delicious preparation:
first a layer of sliced beetroot, then a layer of meat sauce (see
Stracotto, page 34, or the sauce chapter for suggestions). Repeat
twice, ending with a layer of meat sauce and a sprinkling of
Parmesan. Bake at 375°F, 190°C, Gas Mark 5, for 15-20 minutes.
It's absolutely stunning. For best results, you need fresh beetroots, that have been *baked*, not boiled. The texture of the baked
beets is perfect for the casserole (and for salads, and for general
nibbling). Never discard the beet greens. Wash them well, trim
off the stalks and cook and serve the leaves as you would spinach.
Chop the stems and stir fry them in stock.

Whole beetroots

1   Preheat the oven to 400°F, 200°C, Gas Mark 6.
2   Trim the greens away, and wrap the whole, unpeeled beet-
    roots in heavy duty foil, shiny side in (3-4 beetroots may go
    in one package).

3   Bake in the oven for 1-2 hours, until tender. (Timing depends on age and size.) Use a skewer for testing doneness. The skewer should go in easily, but the beetroots should not be mushy.
4   Cool, then trim and slip off the skins.

GRILLED PEPPERS

What fun it is to grill peppers! The idea is to *char* them — either directly on the gas hob, or under the grill. When the burnt skin is removed (it slips right off), the pepper flesh is revealed: tender and supple, sweet with a hint of smokiness, and brilliantly red (or yellow). Keep them covered on a plate in the fridge: they form their own delicious sauce. I never understand why anyone would want to swamp this glory with olive oil — it just obscures the subtlety of the sweet/smoky flavour.

Red and yellow peppers

1   If you have a gas cooker, grill the peppers by placing them directly on the flame of the burner plate. As the peppers blacken and char, turn them with tongs. Alternatively, cut them in half, place under the grill, cut side down, and grill until they blacken and char. I do mean *blackened* and *charred*. They will look absolutely awful, but that is exactly how they should look. Remember: in this case, Burnt is Beautiful.
2   When blackened and charred, enclose the hot peppers in a plastic food bag and leave for 5-10 minutes. Steam will form between the charred skin and the flesh, making peeling much easier. Strip off the charred skin and discard it. (Don't rinse them in water — you will only wash away the lovely smoky flavour.) Discard the cores, seeds and stalks.

GRILLED AUBERGINE

The traditional way with aubergine is to slice them, salt the slices to disgorge any bitterness, dry them and then pan fry the slices in olive oil. No matter how meticulously the slices are salted and drained, they soak up oil like a sponge so that — even though the aubergine itself has minimal Calories and no fat — the oil-soaked slices add hundreds of fat Calories to a dish. Grilling is the answer, and there is absolutely no need to salt (or oil) the slices first. Grilled aubergine is splendid as part of a grilled vegetable platter (see below) or in Aubergine Gratin (page 53), or Aubergine Lasagne (page 96).

---

1 large aubergine, sliced
   crossways, ¼-inch/0.5-cm
   thick

---

1 Preheat the grill to the highest setting.
2 Spread out the aubergine slices in one layer on a non-stick baking sheet. Grill, close to the heat, for 5-7 minutes or until they are tender and speckled with brown. (No need to turn them.)

> 'Almost all Sicilian recipes require that the eggplant
> (aubergine) be fried in olive oil and, given the
> spongelike nature of this vegetable, quite a bit of it.
> Since few inhabitants of the English-speaking world can
> afford an unlimited supply of olive oil, and since frying
> has lost prestige of late, it is not a bad idea to try
> substituting the broiler (grill) for the frying pan.'
>
> Mary Taylor Simeti, *Sicilian Food*

 ## GRILLED COURGETTES

Courgettes can be sliced and grilled exactly as aubergine. Grilled courgette slices make a terrific snack — and you can eat *all you want!*

Approximately 5 medium   crossways, ¼-inch/0.5-cm
   courgettes, slant cut   thick

---

1 Preheat the grill to the highest setting.
2 Spread out the courgette slices in one layer on a non-stick baking sheet. Grill, close to the heat, for 3-5 minutes until tender and speckled with brown. (No need to turn them.)

 ## ANTIPASTO PLATTER OF
GRILLED VEGETABLES

When grilled vegetables are arranged on a large platter, and dressed with a balsamic vinegar-chilli-garlic infusion, or a sweet and sour infusion, the result is a spectacular symphony of taste, colour, texture — really quite over the top. The slightly sweet, slightly charred taste of the vegetables, the piquant taste of the infusion, the texture of the vegetables as they soak up the infusion . . . it's one of the great experiences of Slim Cuisine, Italian Style.

Grilled pepper halves (all colours)	*Pinch crushed dried chillies*
Grilled courgette slices	*½ tablespoon balsamic vinegar*
Grilled aubergine slices	*2-4 cloves garlic, crushed*
10 spring onions, trimmed and sliced thin	*1 pt/570 ml stock*

1   Arrange the grilled pepper halves, courgette slices and aubergine slices on an attractive platter. Take your time, and make the platter of arranged vegetables look like a stunning mosaic.
2   Combine the remaining ingredients in a heavy-bottomed, non-reactive frying pan. Cover and bring to the boil, simmer for 7-10 minutes. Uncover and simmer briskly until the onions are tender and the liquid is thick and syrupy. Pour and scrape the mixture over the grilled vegetables.

ALTERNATIVE INFUSION (SWEET AND SOUR) FOR GRILLED VEGETABLES

1 pt/570 ml stock	*2 tablespoons capers*
1 tablespoon balsamic vinegar	*3 tablespoons sultanas*
2-4 cloves garlic, chopped	*Juice of 1 lemon*

Combine all the ingredients in a non-reactive saucepan and bring to the boil, covered. Boil, covered, for 7 minutes. Uncover and simmer until thick and syrupy. Pour and scrape over the vegetables.

♡ Omit sultanas.

BASIC GLOBE ARTICHOKE PREPARATION

Artichokes are big thistles. The first sight of one at the dinner table can be quite intimidating. How do you eat such a bizarre looking thing? It's fragrant and steamy and probably perfectly delicious, but how on earth do you begin? A large portion of a globe artichoke is totally inedible, but the edible parts are so delicious that all the work (and all the debris) are worthwhile. Only the inside of the large artichoke leaves is edible. So when faced with your first cooked artichoke, stay calm. Begin picking off the leaves one by one with your fingers. Place each leaf in your mouth with the tender meaty part against your upper teeth. Pull against your teeth to scrape off and eat that delicious tender meat. Discard the scraped leaf. (A bowl or plate should be provided on the table for the litter of discarded leaves.)

When all the leaves have been dealt with you will find yourself at the heart. This is your prize: a succulent, luscious reward for battling your way through a thistle in the first place. The heart is eaten with a knife and fork and is — indeed — very good, but it is covered with a hairy, fuzzy 'choke' of extremely prickly and unpleasant texture. The directions that follow tell you how to remove the choke *before* cooking and serving, but you may — in a restaurant — find that you have dutifully scraped and eaten your way through the leaves, only to find yourself faced with the heart, still protected by its daunting covering of choke. Simply — with your spoon — scrape it off, and deposit all of the fuzzy, hairy debris in the litter bowl. Then — in exhausted triumph — tackle the lovely heart with your knife and fork.

♡ ❄ ♉ FOR ARTICHOKE HEARTS:

The hearts, on their own, stuffed with a savoury bread mixture, make a lovely first course, or addition to an antipasto platter.

6 globe artichokes	*Juice of 1 lemon*

1 Bring a large, non-reactive pot of salted water to the boil. Fill a large bowl with cold water and squeeze in the juice of 1 lemon.
2 Cut off the stem of each globe artichoke and trim each base so that they can stand upright. As soon as an artichoke is trimmed, *immediately* drop it into the bowl of acidulated water.
3 When all the artichokes are trimmed, snap off all the tough, outer leaves, and slice off the top inch of each artichoke. As each one is done, drop it back into the acidulated water.
4 Drop the trimmed artichokes into the boiling water, base down, and boil, partially covered, for 25-30 minutes. Drain in

a colander over a large bowl and rinse under cold running water.

5 Pull off all remaining leaves. With a paring knife and a teaspoon, cut away and scrape away all of the fuzzy, hairy choke. Scrape the defuzzed artichoke bottoms carefully so that all vestiges of the choke are gone, and the bottoms are slightly hollow.

6 Save all the leaves for artichoke stock (see below).

♡ᶲ FOR WHOLE ARTICHOKES

When you prepare whole artichokes for stuffing, be kind to yourself and those you feed. Dechoke the heart first, so that the consumption of the cooked, stuffed thistle will be easy and stress-free.

1 Follow steps 1-4 in the previous recipe, but cook the whole artichokes in boiling water for 20 minutes only. Drain, rinse under cold running water and drain again, upside down.

2 Pull the outer leaves out of the artichoke and spread out the remaining leaves. With a small paring knife and a teaspoon, scrape and cut out the hairy choke. The artichokes are now ready for stuffing and baking.

⊞ ⊕ ᶲ Follow steps 1 through 3 (page 49), then place the artichokes in one layer in a shallow microwave-proof dish. If you want whole artichokes for stuffing cook on full power for 10 minutes, if you want the trimmed hearts, microwave on full power for 15 minutes.

ARTICHOKE STOCK

Artichoke leaves make wonderful stock. Simply put them into a *large*, non-reactive pot with plenty of cold water, bring to the boil, and simmer, covered, for approximately 45 minutes. Pour through a colander into a large receptacle, pressing down on the leaves. Let the vivid green stock cool, pour into small containers, and store in the freezer. This simple stock has a wonderfully intense artichoke flavour, and makes a good base for soup and an excellent sauté medium. Try quickly sautéing a mixture of halved dwarf courgettes, strips of cooked artichoke hearts, trimmed, peeled asparagus cut into 1-inch/2.5-cm lengths and strips of peeled red and yellow peppers in this stock. Sauté on high heat, constantly stirring and turning the vegetables, until they are crisp-tender and the stock has cooked down. Exquisite!

FRITTATA

Serves 4-6

A frittata is a round, cushiony filled omelette, served (hot, warm or at room temperature), cut into wedges. A selection of frittatas makes splendid picnic food. A frittata is easily made in an 8-inch/20.5-cm non-stick frying pan with gently sloping sides. If you don't want to flip it over in order to cook the second side, flash it under the grill instead. Although frittatas are usually made with whole eggs, I've eliminated more than half of the yolks, but — if your fillings are good — the quality of the frittata will not suffer.

2 whole eggs	*Salt and freshly ground pepper*
4 egg whites	*to taste*
	Filling of your choice (see note)

1   Beat together the eggs, egg whites, salt and pepper.
2   Put the filling into an 8-inch/20.5-cm non-stick omelette pan. Heat, stirring it around until it sizzles.
3   Pour in the eggs and tilt the pan, allowing the eggs to seep through and around the filling. Give it a few seconds to set on the bottom. Then with a wooden spatula, or a plastic fish slice, push the edges of the eggs toward the centre, working your way around the perimeter, tilting as you go so that the uncooked portion of the egg spreads to the edges of the pan. Shake the pan to keep the frittata moving — you don't want it to stick.
4   When the frittata is set on the bottom, slide it on to a plate. Put another plate over it, and flip it over so that the uncooked side is underneath. Slide it back into the pan, and cook, shaking the pan, until the bottom is cooked (or simply flash it under the grill). Slide out on to a serving plate. To serve, cut into wedges.

Note: **Frittata Fillings:**
Left-over pasta is sublime in a frittata, as are left-over cooked potatoes, or, indeed, any cooked vegetables (courgettes with sun-dried tomatoes, page 58, are especially good). Try as well crumbled cooked sausage (any sausage recipe from this collection).

SPRINGTIME FRITTATA

Serves 4-6

There are excellent quality frozen artichoke hearts available, but they can be difficult to find. Should you be lucky enough to find them in a speciality store near you, they will delight you. No boiling, no scraping the choke, no trimming — what a pleasure! Artichoke hearts are so good, though, that it's worth the trouble to prepare them from scratch. I love the look of this frittata: pale yellow (*very* pale, because of the scant egg yolks) against the variegated green of the vegetables.

3 large cooked artichoke hearts (see page 49) or 6-8 frozen ones sliced into strips	8 oz/225 g shelled peas, fresh or frozen
10 spring onions, trimmed and sliced thin	2 whole eggs
	4 egg whites
½ pt/300 ml artichoke stock or vegetable stock	Salt and freshly ground pepper to taste

1   Combine the sliced artichoke hearts, the spring onions and the stock in a non-stick omelette pan. Simmer, stirring frequently, until the onions and artichokes are tender. Stir in the peas and cook for a minute or two more. By now, the liquid should be about gone.
2   With a fork, beat the whole eggs, the egg whites and the salt and pepper until just blended. Pour the eggs over the vegetable mixture and tilt the pan so that the eggs can seep around the vegetables. Give it a few seconds on a moderate heat to set on the bottom. Then, with a plastic fish slice, push the edges of the eggs towards the centre, working your way around the perimeter and tilting as you go, so that the uncooked portion of the eggs spreads to the edges of the pan. Shake the pan to keep the frittata moving so that it doesn't stick.
3   When the frittata is set on the bottom, slide it on to a plate. Put another plate over it, and flip it over so that the uncooked side is underneath. Slide it back into the pan, and cook, shaking the pan, until the bottom is cooked. Slide out on to a serving plate. To serve, cut into wedges.

POTATO PIZZA

Makes 1 10-inch/25.5-cm pizza

This gorgeous pie, inspired by a traditional Pugliese recipe, has a tender base made from a potato-flour dough, not unlike the dough used to make Potato Gnocchi (page 99). Good tomatoes are essential; if none are available, substitute tinned Italian tomatoes, drained and cut into strips. Serve small wedges of the pie as a first course, or larger ones as a main course.

1¼ lb/550 g baking potatoes, baked and scooped out of their shells, or boiled in their skins until tender and then peeled
4 oz/110 g sponge flour
Salt and freshly ground pepper to taste

10 medium-sized fresh ripe tomatoes, peeled, seeded, juiced and cut into strips
5 oz/150 g mozzarella cheese, shredded
2 tablespoons grated Parmesan cheese
2 tablespoons shredded fresh basil

---

1 Preheat the oven to 400°F, 200°C, Gas Mark 6.
2 Push the potatoes through a ricer or a mouli (makes 1½ pts/900 ml mashed potatoes).
3 In a bowl, with your hands, mix the potatoes, flour, salt and pepper to a smooth, not too sticky paste. Add a bit more flour if necessary, but remember − the mixture should be *slightly* sticky.
4 Lightly flour your work surface and roll out the dough with a rolling pin to generously fit a 10-11-inch/25.5-28-cm non-stick pie or quiche dish. Loosen the underside of the dough with a palette knife and fold it in half, then into quarters. Centre it on the dish and unfold it. Press it down, and push the edges all around to form a crimped edge.
5 Cut the tomatoes into strips and lay them on the potatoes. Sprinkle with the mozzarella, Parmesan and basil.
6 Bake for 25-30 minutes, or until bubbly and brown.

♡Omit mozzarella, or use rendered mozzarella (page 8).

AUBERGINE GRATIN

Melanzane Parmigiana (Aubergine-Cheese gratin) is one of the staples of the Naples-inspired American-Italian cuisine on which I cut my gastronomic teeth. (That's a refined way of saying that I chomped my way through *lots* of it in my younger days.) For a traditional *Melanzane Parmigiana*, slices of aubergine are fried in oceans of olive oil (I'm not exaggerating all that much – aubergines soak up oil like a sponge), then layered with full-fat cheeses and tomato sauce, and baked. Some versions add a layer of cream sauce (*besciamella*) as well – the texture contrasts of the fried aubergine, the melted cheeses and the creamy sauce are the height of gastronomic sensuality. Of course, it was also fattening as hell and – from my present vantage point – not particularly digestible. I'm very pleased with the Slim Cuisine version: the aubergine slices are grilled, the cheeses are medium-fat, and the cream sauce is replaced by quark and beaten egg whites. The quark-egg-white layer rises like a soufflé but remains seductively creamy: the sensuality of the texture contrasts remain, but the total effect is one of delicacy.

---

1 lb/450 g quark
½ lb/225 g Italian-style, medium-fat mozzarella cheese
Salt and freshly ground pepper to taste
3 egg whites, beaten to firm peaks

3 small aubergines, cut into ¼-½-inch/0.5-1-cm slices, grilled (see page 46)
1 pt/570 ml Quick Tomato Sauce with Capers (see page 109)
4-5 tablespoons Parmesan cheese

---

1   Preheat the oven to 400°F, 200°C, Gas Mark 6.
2   Combine the quark, mozzarella cheese, salt and pepper in the bowl of a food processor. Process until well amalgamated. Transfer to a bowl. Stir in one quarter of the beaten egg whites, fold in the remainder. Cut each aubergine slice in half.
3   Put a thin layer of the tomato sauce into the bottom of a gratin dish (12 inch × 7 inch/30.5 × 18 cm), cover with a layer of overlapping aubergine slices. Spread on the quark-cheese mixture and sprinkle with 2 tablespoons of Parmesan cheese. Top with another layer of aubergines, then the remaining tomato sauce and finally the 2 tablespoons Parmesan cheese.
4   Bake in the oven, covered, for 15 minutes, uncovered for 10-15 minutes. Allow to rest on a rack for 10-15 minutes before serving. Serve cut into squares.

54

Italian meals are symphonies of taste and texture: from left to right:
beef rolls filled with Parma ham and Parmesan, served with broccoli
polenta; grilled pork steaks filled with sage and mozzarella cheese,
served with potato peperonata.

Beautiful salads are like edible folk art: clockwise from bottom left: roasted pepper, tomato and mozzarella cheese salad; beetroot-rocket salad; tomato-peach salad.

Variations:

❄️ AUBERGINE-GARLIC GRATIN

In step 2, process roasted garlic purée (I use the purée from a head of garlic) into the quark and mozzarella cheese.

❄️ SIMPLE AUBERGINE GRATIN

Omit the quark layer: simply layer aubergine slices, tomato sauce, a bit of shredded mozzarella and a bit of grated Parmesan. The top layers should be aubergine, sauce and grated Parmesan. Bake as directed in the main recipe.

♡ Omit Parmesan cheese and mozzarella (or use rendered mozzarella cheese, page 8).

❄️ STUFFED COURGETTES

Makes 8 pieces

Courgettes (*zucchini*), when halved and hollowed with a teaspoon, make perfect little boats for stuffing. (If you were to do this with marrows, you really would have boats; you could set out to sea in them.) Serve one as a first course, or 2 or more as a vegetarian main dish.

4 medium-sized courgettes	*Pinch crushed dried chillies*
Approximately 1 pt/570 ml stock	*¼ pt/150 ml dry vermouth*
1 medium onion, chopped	*½ pt/300 ml cooked long-grain*
3 cloves garlic, chopped	*rice*
3 olives in brine, drained and	*3 tablespoons grated Parmesan*
sliced off the stone	*cheese*
3 dry pack sun-dried tomatoes,	*Freshly ground pepper to taste*
snipped (use scissors) —	*2-3 tablespoons chopped fresh*
optional	*parsley*

1   Preheat the oven to 350°F, 180°C, Gas Mark 4.
2   Trim the courgettes. Cut in half lengthways. With a teaspoon, scrape out the centre flesh, so that you have 8 courgette 'boats'. Roughly chop the centres and set aside.

3   In a square baking dish arrange the courgettes, skin side up. Sprinkle in 1-2 tablespoons of the stock. Microwave at full power for 3 minutes until just beginning to lose their rawness. Let stand for 1 minute. Set aside. (If you have no microwave, steam the halves for approximately 5 minutes.)
4   Put the chopped courgette centres into a heavy-bottomed frying pan along with the onion, garlic, olives, sun-dried tomatoes, chillies, ½ pt/300 ml stock and the vermouth. Cover and boil for about 5 minutes. Uncover and sauté until the onion is tender, and the liquid is almost gone.
5   Stir in the rice and another 3-4 tablespoons of stock. Cook, stirring until the rice is well amalgamated with the other ingredients and the additional stock is absorbed. Stir in 2 tablespoons of the cheese, the pepper and the parsley.
6   Coat the bottom of a baking dish with a bit of stock. Arrange the courgette boats on the stock in one layer. Fill each with the rice mixture. Sprinkle with the remaining Parmesan cheese.
7   Bake for 20 minutes covered, then for 10 minutes uncovered, until nicely browned. Serve at once.

Courgette Blossoms

Courgette blossoms are beautiful to look at and exquisite to eat: alas, they are only available if you grow your own, or are lucky enough to live near a small farm that grows courgettes. I am lucky enough to live near Snakehall Farm (the Prospect Trust). During the courgette season I or one of my helpers shows up at their barn door early in the morning to collect blooms. The Italians (and the French, and the Mexicans) really appreciate courgette blossoms – during their season you see them piled on summertime market stalls, listed on restaurant menus and served forth in home kitchens. Traditionally, the blossoms are stuffed with a savoury mixture, then battered and fried. It's bad enough (in fact, it's the height of barbarity) obscuring these delicately textured and flavoured, exquisitely graceful yellow flowers in batter, but to then *fry* them? True, the batter is usually fairly light and the finished fritters brittle and crisp, but why on earth should such a delicate flower end its life as a glorified potato crisp? How much more civilized to fill the blossoms and then steam them: the taste of the blossom, the beauty of its shape and colour, the sheer exhilaration of eating a delicious flower – none of these impressions will be blunted by a blanket of batter or the intrusive flavour of butter or oil.

The male blossoms grow on stalks; they look enchanting when served raw as a garnish, or as an addition to a leafy salad. The female blossoms grow on the courgettes. The following recipe will show you how to stuff the blossom (still attached to the courgette) and steam blossom and courgette together. There are few seasonal feasts to equal this one.

♡ 🧸 🥕 COURGETTES WITH THEIR MUSHROOM-FILLED BLOSSOMS

Makes 4

I was in Nice just before beginning work on this book, when the markets were overflowing with tiny courgettes and their golden blossoms. My hotel room had no kitchen. Wandering through such a market with no way to release — through cooking — the resulting frenzy of vegetable enthusiasm is a good way to have a nervous breakdown. Back home again, I impatiently waited for courgette-blossom time to arrive in England so that I could plunder my local organic vegetable/herb farm (Snakehall Farm in Reach) of their supply. If *you* have a source of tiny courgettes and their flowers, try steaming them as described here. Serve them unadorned, or on a light bed of any of the tomato sauces in the sauce chapter. Serve as a first course, or a summer lunch.

4 tiny courgettes with their blossoms still attached, carefully rinsed in cold water	*Approximately 4 generous tablespoons Intense Mushroom Pâté (see page 115)*

1 Carefully remove the pistil from each blossom. With a small sharp knife, carefully — starting just below the blossom — slice the courgette into 4-5 slices, but *do not separate* the courgette from the blossom. The courgette will still be intact, but you will be able to fan out the sliced portion.
2 Fill each blossom with a very generous tablespoon of the mushroom mixture. Place the courgettes, evenly spaced, on a heat-proof plate. Bring water to a boil in your steamer arrangement (see page 58). Put the plate in the steamer, cover, and steam for about 15 minutes, until the courgettes are crisp-tender; that is, not at all mushy, but not at all raw either. Test just below the blossom with a thin skewer or cake tester. With a fish slice, carefully transfer each to a plate. Gently fan out the segments of each courgette. Serve at once.

Variation:

COURGETTES WITH THEIR SPINACH-FILLED BLOSSOMS

Follow the above recipe, but substitute the Spinach-Ricotta mixture on page 128 for the mushroom mixture.

Steamers

A big wok with a lid is perfect for steaming the courgettes. Some woks come with a steaming rack; if not improvise one by placing a small overturned heat-proof bowl or plate on the bottom of the wok. Pour in boiling water. Set the courgettes with their stuffed blossoms on a larger heat-proof plate (the plate should fit nicely in the wok). Put the courgette plate on the rack. Obviously, the boiling water should reach a level just below the plate. Cover the wok tightly and steam. (Replenish the water if it starts to boil away.)

COURGETTES WITH SUN-DRIED TOMATOES AND GARLIC

Yields 1pt/570 ml

Courgettes, cut into strips and sautéed in stock with morsels of sun-dried tomatoes, black olives, garlic and a bit of chilli, are delicious served hot, or cold, stuffed into a Frittata (page 51) or even tossed into pasta.

---

1 lb/450 g courgettes	½ pt/300 ml stock
6 black olives in brine, sliced off the stones	6 ripe tomatoes, peeled and seeded, cut into strips
2-3 cloves garlic, crushed	Freshly ground pepper to taste
1 small chilli pepper, minced, or a pinch of crushed dried chillies	2 tablespoons shredded basil leaves
6-7 sun-dried tomatoes, snipped (use scissors)	4 tablespoons chopped fresh parsley

---

1   Wash and trim the courgettes, and cut them into strips 1½ inch/3.5 cm long and ¼-½ inch/0.5-1 cm thick. Put them in a non-reactive frying pan or wok with the olives, garlic, chilli, sun-dried tomatoes and half the stock. Bring to the boil. Cook, stirring and tossing the ingredients, for 3-4 minutes.
2   Add the tomatoes and the remaining stock. Season to taste (you will probably need little or no salt because the olives are

salty). Cook on a moderate heat, stirring occasionally until the courgettes are tender (but not at all mushy) and the liquid and tomatoes have cooked down to a sauce. Sprinkle in the herbs, stir and cook for a minute or so longer.

🧸 ♡ Omit olives.

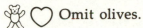 ## COURGETTES WITH MUSHROOMS

Yields 1½ pts/900 ml

The microwave is very good to courgettes; they emerge from the machine bursting with flavour and freshness. Here, the courgettes are mixed with a mushroom paste, microwaved briefly, and then enriched with a light sprinkling of Parmesan.

1½ lb/700 g small courgettes, washed, trimmed and sliced ¾ inch/1.5 cm thick	3-4 heaped tablespoons Intense Mushroom Pâté (see page 115) 2-3 tablespoons grated Parmesan cheese

1   Combine the courgette slices and mushroom mixture in a 9-10-inch/23-25.5-cm square, 2-inch/5-cm deep microwave-safe baking dish. Cover with cling film and microwave on full power for 5 minutes. Uncover and stir, re-cover and cook for another 3 minutes. Uncover and sprinkle with the grated cheese, re-cover and let stand for 5 minutes.

♡ 🧸 Omit Parmesan cheese.

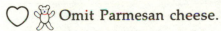 ## STUFFED WHOLE ARTICHOKES

My friend Anne Masselli remembers the stuffed artichokes her grandmother used to bake by the panful, several times a week. 'No matter what I do,' she laments, 'my artichokes never taste as good as my Nonna's did!' And I'll always remember *my* very first artichoke, back in the early sixties, prepared by another friend, Donna Zenobia Saffir. It was stuffed with a bread-mint-garlic-olive oil stuffing. I thought that artichoke was one of the most delicious things I had ever eaten, not to mention the most fun. After all, the first time one devours a thistle has to be a major life event. The bread stuffing is an amalgamation of Anne's descriptions of her Nonna's masterpiece, and my memory of my first artichoke. The olive oil has been replaced with a few slivers of olive and a sprinkling of olive brine, but the garlic, the mint, the intense artichoke flavour — they are all there. Use it to stuff a whole artichoke, or try one of the other stuffings, listed below.

Whole artichokes	Bread stuffing (see below)
Artichoke stock (see page 50) or other stock	

1 Prepare artichokes for stuffing according to directions on page 50.
2 Preheat the oven to 350°F, 180°C, Gas Mark 4.
3 Pour a few fluid ounces of artichoke stock into a shallow, non-reactive baking dish that will hold the artichokes in one layer. Place the artichokes in the dish. Push a generous amount of stuffing (see suggestions below) into the centre of the artichokes. Slip some of the stuffing in between the leaves. Sprinkle a bit of stock over each artichoke.
4 Bake, loosely covered, for 15 minutes. Uncover and sprinkle with a bit more stock if the stuffing looks dry. Bake for 10-15 minutes uncovered. Check for tenderness by piercing the bottom with the tip of a paring knife. If necessary, bake a few minutes longer. Serve hot or cold.

STUFFING

Makes ½ pt/300 ml

8 tablespoons fresh parsley, chopped	1 teaspoon olive brine
3 tablespoons fresh mint, chopped	4-5 olives, sliced off the stone
2 oz/50 g good white bread, crumbled	Pepper to taste
2-3 large cloves garlic, minced	3 tablespoons artichoke stock
	1 tablespoon balsamic vinegar

1 Mix thoroughly the parsley, mint, bread, garlic, olive brine, olives and pepper. Sprinkle in stock and vinegar. Mix well.

♡Omit olives.

Other Suggestions for Stuffing Artichokes
Intense Mushroom Pâté (page 115)
Spinach-Ricotta (page 128)
Sausage Sauce (page 113)
Stracotto (page 34)

STUFFED ARTICHOKE HEARTS

Makes 6 stuffed artichoke hearts

Artichoke hearts filled with the bread-mint-garlic stuffing make a vibrant first course, or light lunch.

6 artichoke hearts (prepared according to directions on page 49) *Bread Stuffing (page 60)*	*Approximately 4 fl oz/110 ml artichoke stock* *6 tablespoons Parmesan cheese*

1 Preheat the oven to 350°F, 180°C, Gas Mark 4.
2 Put the artichoke hearts into a baking dish that will hold them in one layer. Fill each with some of the stuffing. Tuck the remaining stuffing over and around them. Sprinkle each stuffed artichoke heart with a bit of artichoke stock. Pour in stock to come about an inch/2.5 cm up the sides of the dish. Cover with foil. Bake for 20-25 minutes.
3 Uncover. Sprinkle the cheese evenly over the contents of the baking dish. Re-cover and bake for another 20 minutes, until the artichoke hearts are tender and the cheese has melted. Serve at once.

♡ Omit olives from the stuffing, and omit Parmesan cheese.

 ## POTATO-WILD MUSHROOM GRATIN

Serves 6-8

The secret of success with this gratin is in the slicing: slice the unpeeled potatoes *paper thin* on a mandoline, or with the slicing disc of a food processor. The tissue-thin slices are layered with mushroom paste, moistened with a bit of stock, sprinkled with Parmesan cheese and baked until the potatoes are tender and saturated with the woodsy flavour and aroma of the mushrooms. *Earthy* is the word that comes to mind.

Approximately 1¼ lbs/550 g baking potatoes, scrubbed but unpeeled *Freshly ground pepper* *Approximately 6 tablespoons Parmesan cheese*	*Approximately 6-8 tablespoons stock* *½ pt/300 ml Intense Mushroom Pâté (see page 115)*

1   Preheat the oven to 400°F, 200°C, Gas Mark 6.
2   Slice the potatoes as thin as possible on a mandoline.
3   Put a thin layer of potatoes on the bottom of a 12 × 7 inch/30.5 × 18 cm gratin dish. Sprinkle with freshly ground pepper and 2 tablespoons of Parmesan cheese. Moisten with a few tablespoons of stock. Spread some of the mushroom pâté over the potatoes. Sprinkle on another tablespoon of stock. Repeat once more.
4   Top with a layer of potatoes. Sprinkle with freshly ground pepper and 2 tablespoons of Parmesan cheese. With a pastry brush, brush this top layer with stock. Bake for 1 hour. During this time, brush the top layer with stock 2 or 3 times. When the bottom layers are tender, and the top layer is browned and slightly crisp, the gratin is done. Serve at once. (To serve, cut into squares.)

♡ Omit Parmesan cheese.

 # GARLIC POTATOES

Makes 1½ pts/900 ml

Garlic and potatoes: they go together like Bogart and Bacall, like Fred and Ginger. I once wrote an entire book about garlic, and another entire one about potatoes. If given the chance, I'm sure I could manage yet another volume about the two of them *put together*. This recipe makes the best of both down-to-earth ingredients. They are simply pan-simmered in stock until the potatoes are tender and imbued with the essence of garlic, then cloaked with a light mantle of just melted Parmesan cheese.

2 large baking potatoes	*Salt and freshly ground pepper*
3-4 large cloves garlic, crushed	*to taste*
Approximately ½ pt/300 ml	*2-3 tablespoons grated*
stock	*Parmesan cheese*

1   Slice the potatoes ¼-inch/0.5-cm thick, then halve each slice crossways. Toss them in a large frying pan with the garlic, half the stock and the salt and pepper. Bring to the boil, immediately reduce the heat and simmer, covered, for 15-20 minutes, uncovering to stir occasionally. Add more stock as needed.
2   After 15-20 minutes, when the potatoes are almost tender, uncover and continue to cook, adding stock as needed to

prevent burning, until the potatoes are completely tender. Spread the potatoes out evenly in the pan, sprinkle evenly with cheese, cover and let sit for 5 minutes on lowest heat. Uncover — the cheese will have melted. Serve at once.

♡ Omit the cheese.

BRAISED NEW POTATOES WITH MUSHROOMS

Makes 1½ pts/900 ml

The Slim Cuisine infusion of garlic, olives, sun-dried tomatoes and spring onions works particularly well with new potatoes; they soak up the hearty Italian flavour like thirsty sponges, yet their own wonderful flavour is not obscured. The mushrooms add their own earthiness.

½ pt/300 ml stock	Pinch or 2 crushed dried chillies
5 fl oz/150 ml water	(to taste)
2 tablespoons dry white	4 black olives, sliced off the
vermouth	stone
10 spring onions, trimmed, the	1 lb/450 g whole tiny new
white portions minced, the	potatoes
green portions thinly sliced	2 teaspoons of the olive brine
2 cloves garlic, minced	Freshly ground pepper to taste
4-6 sun-dried tomatoes, snipped	4½ oz/120 g button mushrooms,
(use scissors) — optional	halved or quartered
	Chopped fresh parsley

1 Combine half of the stock, 5 fl oz/150 ml of water, and the vermouth with the white parts of the spring onions, the garlic, the sun-dried tomatoes, the chillies and the olives. Cover and bring to the boil. Boil for 5-7 minutes. Uncover and simmer briskly for another few minutes until the onion and tomato pieces are tender.
2 Stir in the potatoes, olive brine and the remaining stock. Season with freshly ground pepper. Simmer, partially covered, for 5 minutes. Stir in the mushrooms. Simmer, partially covered, for 15-20 minutes, or until the potatoes are tender, and the liquid almost gone. If the liquid cooks down before the potatoes and mushrooms are done, add a little stock or water. Garnish with parsley and a scattering of the sliced green portions of the spring onions.

♡ Omit olives.

LEMON BRAISED POTATOES

Makes 1½ pts/900 ml

Potatoes and lemon are another culinary marriage made in heaven. The potatoes are imbued with lemon and garlic, and flecked with olive slivers and parsley.

½ pt/300 ml stock	2 cloves of garlic, coarsely
Juice of 1 lemon	chopped
4 black olives in brine, drained	1½ lb/700 g new potatoes,
and sliced off their stones	quartered
1 tablespoon of the olive brine	Freshly ground pepper to taste
	Chopped parsley for garnish

1 In a non-reactive, heavy-bottomed casserole or frying pan, combine the stock, half of the lemon juice, the olives, olive brine and garlic. Stir in the potatoes. Bring to the boil. Boil, covered for 10 minutes or until the potatoes are almost tender.
2 Uncover. Grind in some pepper. Simmer briskly, uncovered, stirring occasionally, until the liquid is greatly reduced and syrupy. Squeeze in the remaining lemon juice. Cook a few more minutes stirring frequently, until the potatoes are tender and the liquid about gone. Serve warm or at room temperature, sprinkled with fresh parsley.

♡ Omit olives.

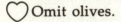 **PEPERONATA WITH NEW POTATOES**

Makes 1¼ pts/700 ml

Peperonata is a mélange of red peppers and onions, pan fried in olive oil. If the peppers are peeled, and then pan fried in stock, they cook into a melting, saucy richness, despite the total absence of oil. New potatoes are a satisfying addition to Peperonata.

6 large red peppers	6 fl oz/175 ml stock
1 large Spanish onion, skinned,	1 tablespoon drained capers
halved and cut into thin half-	Freshly ground pepper to taste
moons	12 oz/350 g halved new potatoes
2 cloves garlic, finely chopped	2 tablespoons chopped fresh
2 fl oz/50 ml dry white vermouth	parsley
Juice of 1 lemon	

1   Halve the peppers, remove the stalks, cores and seeds, then cut them into their natural sections. Peel with a swivel-bladed vegetable peeler. Cut each piece into strips about ½-inch/1-cm wide.
2   Combine the peppers, onion, garlic, vermouth, half the lemon juice, the stock and capers in a heavy bottomed, non-reactive frying pan. Grind in some pepper. Bring to the boil and toss and turn the vegetables in the stock for a few moments. Stir in the potatoes. Cook, stirring occasionally, until the liquid has cooked down considerably. Stir in the remaining lemon juice.
3   Let the vegetables 'fry' in their own juices until the potatoes are tender. Add a bit more stock as needed. Stir in the parsley.

FRIED PEPPERS

Makes 1 pt/570 ml

Fried peppers can be made with red peppers only, or a mixture of red and yellow. If green peppers are the only kind available, use them: the result will be less sweet (and of course not nearly as colourful), but still very good to eat. Fried peppers can be served as a vegetable side dish but they are best as a lavish garnish: to Veal Milanese, Fettine, meatballs, sausages, or in scrambled eggs (page 66). They are also exceptionally good tossed into freshly cooked pasta.

1 onion, peeled, cut in half and sliced into thin half-moons	Pinch or two (to taste) crushed dried chillies
4-5 sun-dried tomatoes, snipped (use scissors) – optional	1 pt/570 ml stock
	¼ pt/150 ml water
4 black olives in brine, drained and sliced off their stones	2 red peppers, peeled and cut into ½-inch/1-cm wide strips
1 teaspoon of the olive brine	2 yellow peppers, peeled and cut
1-2 cloves garlic, crushed	into ½-inch/1-cm wide strips

1   Combine the onion slices, sun-dried tomatoes, olives, olive brine, garlic, chillies and ½ pt/300 ml stock mixed with ¼ pt/150 ml water. Cover and boil for 5-7 minutes. Uncover and simmer briskly until the onions are tender and lightly browned and the liquid about gone.
2   Add the peppers and the remaining stock. Simmer briskly,

uncovered, stirring and tossing frequently until the peppers are tender and bathed in a thick, syrupy sauce.

 Omit olives.

PEPPERS AND EGGS

Serves 4

As in the frittatas, I get rid of more than half the egg yolks, so that a big, satisfying plate of scrambled eggs with peppers has a minimal dose of fat and cholesterol. If there is a history of high blood cholesterol and heart disease in your family, forget whole eggs altogether, otherwise, the *occasional* whole egg should do no harm.

2 whole eggs	*Salt and freshly ground pepper*
3 egg whites	*to taste*
½ pt/300 ml fried peppers (page 65)	*1-2 tablespoons chopped parsley*

1   Lightly beat the eggs and whites. Stir in the peppers and salt and pepper. Stir in the parsley.
2   Heat a non-stick omelette pan or non-stick frying pan. When moderately hot, pour in the eggs and let sit for a few seconds. With a plastic fish slice, gently push the eggs towards the centre, working all around the edges of the pan. When the eggs are gently scrambled, they are done.

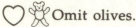 # GRILLED MUSHROOMS

In Italy, large porcini mushrooms − in season − are grilled (often on a wood fire) to tenderness. Last time I was in Rome, it was the height of the porcini season, and I ate them every day (sometimes twice a day). Luigi's on the Fulham Road, my favourite London Italian Deli, grill field mushrooms − they don't have the wild woodsiness of porcini, but they are meaty and good. Luigi does a marvellous sandwich: ciabatta rolls filled with a giant grilled mushroom, a slice of mozzarella cheese and a leaf of tender lettuce. Fresh shiitake mushrooms can be substituted for porcini − although smallish, they have a dark, wild taste that field mushrooms lack. But large grilled field mushrooms, brushed with balsamic vinegar, are terrific in sandwiches.

A few tablespoons of stock
1 tablespoon balsamic vinegar
1 teaspoon olive brine (see page
    4) optional
Large mushrooms, cleaned and
    stemmed (fresh porcini are
    ideal − fresh, stemmed

shiitake mushrooms can be
    substituted, or field
    mushrooms)
Spring onion-garlic-olive
    infusion (see page 4)

1   Combine the stock, vinegar and olive brine.
2   Remove the stems from the mushrooms. Place them on a rack
    in the grill pan. Brush with the stock and vinegar.
3   Grill for approximately 5 minutes on each side, brushing
    occasionally with the stock and vinegar.
4   Sprinkle some of the infusion over each mushroom. Serve as
    a first course, or as a filling for baguettes, ciabatta rolls or
    focaccia.

♡ 🐻 Omit olives from the infusion.

♡🐻🕐❄️🥕 BALSAMIC BRAISED MUSHROOMS

Makes 1 pt/570 ml

This is a dark, wild mushroom tasting ragoût that I like to serve
with meatballs or sausages and tomato sauce. Make it even
woodsier by adding reconstituted dried porcini mushrooms and
their soaking liquid.

1½ lb/700 g assorted mushrooms
    (shiitake, brown cap, and
    cultivated), quartered
2 fl oz/50 ml stock

2 fl oz/50 ml medium Marsala or
    sherry
2 dashes soy sauce
1 tablespoon balsamic vinegar
Freshly ground pepper to taste

1   Combine all the ingredients in a heavy-bottomed non-
    reactive frying pan. Bring to the boil. Cook, stirring occa-
    sionally. The mushrooms will render quite a bit of juice.
    Continue cooking, stirring occasionally until the mushrooms
    are cooked and the liquid is almost gone. Do not allow them
    to stick or burn. Serve hot or at room temperature. Store in
    the refrigerator.

SAUTÉED FRENCH BEANS

Makes 1½ pts/900 ml

First steam the beans, then toss them in the Slim Cuisine Italian infusion, add some shredded basil ... even vegetable haters have been known to gobble them compulsively. In season I prepare these with Italian purple beans (Viola Cornetti — a traditional climbing bean from Italy) and they are exquisite, but you will get excellent results with the garden variety.

1 lb/450 g French beans, topped and tailed and destrung if necessary	3-4 black olives sliced off their stones
10 fl oz/300 ml stock	1 tablespoon balsamic vinegar
1-2 cloves garlic, crushed	Freshly ground pepper to taste
Pinch crushed dried chillies	6-7 fresh basil leaves, shredded
3-4 sun-dried tomatoes, snipped (use scissors) — optional	

1   Steam the beans until crisp-tender. Rinse under cold water, drain well and set aside.
2   Pour stock into a heavy, non-reactive frying pan. Add the garlic, chillies, sun-dried tomatoes, olives and balsamic vinegar. Boil, covered, for 4-5 minutes until reduced by half. Toss in the beans.
3   Toss and cook for 2-3 minutes. Season with pepper and stir in the basil. Stir and cook for 4 minutes or so more. Serve warm or at room temperature.

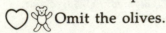 Omit the olives.

Pasta Suggestion:
Serve pasta quills tossed with one of the tomato sauces (see sauce chapter), Stir-Fried Green Beans and roasted red and yellow pepper strips.

OVEN-BRAISED FENNEL

Makes 1 pt/570 ml

Fennel has a haunting anise flavour; as far as I am concerned, that's the whole *point* of fennel. Many recipes direct the cook to blanch the fennel first, in order to dull that deliciously distinctive flavour. Don't do it! If you want to serve fennel that doesn't really taste like fennel, then serve *celery* for heaven's sake. But if you share my passion for all things anise flavoured, you'll love this braising method. When they are cooked, they are meltingly tender, compellingly anisey, and richly glazed.

2 bulbs fennel, trimmed and cut in half lengthwise, then each half cut into wedges approximately ½-inch/1-cm wide	*4 fl oz/110 ml stock* *Freshly ground pepper* *3 tablespoons Parmesan cheese*

1 Preheat the oven to 350°F, 180°C, Gas Mark 4.
2 Arrange fennel in one layer (cut side down) in a baking dish. Pour over 4 fl oz/110 ml stock. Season with pepper. Sprinkle evenly with 3 tablespoons Parmesan cheese.
3 Bake uncovered for 45 minutes. The fennel will become meltingly tender and the stock will have cooked almost completely away, leaving a rich glaze. Serve at once.

♡ Omit cheese.

 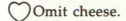

BRAISED BROCCOLI

Makes 1 pt/570 ml

This is prepared according to old-fashioned Italian home cookery. The broccoli loses its bright green colour and is cooked to tenderness, although *not* to mush. The vegetable soaks up the flavours of the piquant, sweet and sour braising ingredients, but keeps its own taste, too. It's hard to stop eating this one: my tasters and I found ourselves eating the lemony broccoli, with our fingers, right out of the pan.

1 large bunch (approximately 14 oz/400 g) broccoli *3 black olives in brine, drained, sliced off the stones* *Pinch or 2 crushed dried chillies* *½ tablespoon drained capers* *2 cloves garlic, crushed* *2-3 sun-dried tomatoes, snipped (use scissors) — optional*	*Juice of approximately 1½ lemons* *Slivered zest of ½ lemon* *Approximately 1 pt/570 ml stock* *½ teaspoon each caper brine and olive brine* *Freshly ground pepper to taste*

1   Wash the broccoli and cut the florets from the stalk – set the florets aside.
2   With a paring knife peel the main stalk and the smaller stalks. Cut the main stalk into quarters lengthwise. Slice the quarters and the small stalks.
3   In a heavy bottomed non-reactive frying pan (or a wok) combine the sliced stalks, olives, chillies, capers, garlic, sun-dried tomatoes, juice of ½ lemon, the lemon rind, ½ pint/300 ml stock and the brines. Bring to the boil. Simmer briskly, covered, for 7-10 minutes, until the liquid is greatly reduced.
4   Stir in the broccoli florets, remaining stock, juice of ½ lemon and the pepper. Simmer, partially covered, stirring occasionally, until the broccoli is tender (with just the merest hint of a crunch) and the liquid is greatly reduced. (If, during the simmering, the liquid cooks away too fast, add a bit more as needed.) Taste and add a bit more lemon juice if you think it is necessary. Serve warm or at room temperature.

♡ Omit the olives.

♡ 🐻 🕐 🥕 **BRAISED VEGETABLES**

Makes 2 pts/1.1 l

These vegetables are very simply braised to tenderness in stock. The peeled peppers help form the delicious, clinging sauce that bathes the finished dish.

2 heads cauliflower, trimmed and broken into large florets	thickly sliced
	2 cloves garlic, crushed
2 red and 2 yellow peppers, seeded, cored, peeled and cut into 1-inch/2.5-cm wide strips	½ pt/300 ml stock
	Salt and freshly ground pepper to taste
	4 tablespoons chopped fresh
½ lb/225 g mushrooms,	parsley

1   Combine the vegetables and garlic in a heavy-bottomed frying pan. Pour in the stock. Season to taste. Cover and cook for 3-4 minutes.
2   Uncover. Cook over a high heat, stirring occasionally, until the liquid is cooked away, the vegetables are tender and the cauliflower is beginning to brown. Stir in the parsley. Serve at once.

BRAISED CABBAGE AND BEANS

Makes approximately 2½ pts/1.4 l

This sustaining and warming winter vegetable dish is usually prepared with *pancetta* — Italian cured bacon. It's hard to find (and it's rather fatty), therefore I have substituted unsmoked lean back bacon. The olive oil has been deleted as well, but the Slim Cuisine olive-garlic infusion gives the dish plenty of character. Cabbage is good food; so are beans; put together they are even better.

---

2 black olives in brine, drained and sliced off their stones
1 onion, cut in half and sliced into thin half-moons
3 cloves garlic, crushed
Pinch or 2 of crushed dried chillies
2 slices unsmoked lean back bacon, trimmed of all fat and diced
1 pt/570 ml stock
1 small savoy cabbage (about 1 lb/450 g) trimmed of tough outer leaves, cored and coarsely shredded (use the slicing disc on the food processor for ease and speed)
1 tablespoon tomato purée
1 tin Borlotti beans (15 oz/425 g), drained and rinsed
Freshly ground pepper to taste
2-3 tablespoons chopped fresh parsley

---

1 Combine the olives, onion, garlic, dried chilli, bacon and 4 fl oz/110 ml stock in a heavy, deep frying pan. Cover and bring to the boil. Reduce the heat a bit, and simmer briskly for 5 minutes. Uncover and cook until the onions are browning and the liquid is about gone.
2 Add the shredded cabbage and stir to coat with the onion mixture. Stir together the remaining stock and the tomato purée and add to the cabbage. Cover and cook for 20 minutes, uncovering to stir occasionally.
3 Stir in the beans and season with pepper. Stir and cook for 3-4 minutes more. Stir in the parsley.

♡ Omit olives and bacon.

🥕 Omit bacon.

CAPONATA

Makes 1 pt/570 ml

Caponata is a sweet and sour amalgamation of aubergines, tomatoes, capers and raisins, often served as part of an antipasto selection. It's marvellous spread on to crusty Country Bread (page 120), or served as an accompaniment to Polpettone (page 34) or Beef Rollantine with Parma Ham and Sage (page 23).

4-5 *black olives in brine, drained and sliced off the stone*	2 *tins (14 oz/400 g each) whole tomatoes, drained and cut into strips*
2 *tablespoons drained capers*	*Salt and freshly ground pepper to taste*
1-2 *tablespoons raisins*	
3-4 *cloves crushed garlic*	
1-2 *good pinches crushed, dried chillies*	2-3 *tablespoons shredded fresh basil leaves*
½ *pt/300 ml stock*	4-5 *tablespoons chopped fresh parsley*
¼ *pt/150 ml dry red wine*	
1 *small (approximately 9 oz/250 g) aubergine, unpeeled and diced*	

1 Combine the olives, capers, raisins, garlic, chillies, stock and wine in a large, non-reactive flame-proof casserole or saucepan. Cover and bring to the boil. Boil for 5-7 minutes.
2 Add the aubergine and tomato strips; season to taste. Simmer, uncovered, for 20 minutes. Stir in the herbs and simmer, stirring occasionally, for 10 minutes more. Serve cool or at room temperature.

Omit olives and raisins.

❄ 🥕ITALIAN ROOT-VEGETABLE GRATIN

Italian ingredients and English ingredients combined with an Italian-flavour infusion make an aromatic, deeply flavoured, puréed vegetable gratin. When it's available, I add pumpkin to the baked vegetables, with excellent results.

9 *carrots*	1 *pinch dried oregano*
3 *turnips*	1 *onion, coarsely chopped*
1 *swede, quartered*	1 *head fennel, trimmed and coarsely chopped*
1 *head garlic*	

15 spring onions, trimmed and sliced	½ pt/300 ml stock
4-5 sun-dried tomatoes, snipped (use scissors) — optional	Salt and freshly ground pepper to taste
Pinch crushed dried chillies	2 tablespoons freshly grated Parmesan cheese
1 teaspoon fennel seeds	Approximately 4 fl oz/110 ml skimmed milk

---

1 Preheat the oven to 425°F, 220°C, Gas Mark 7.
2 Loosely wrap the root vegetables and head of garlic in foil. (Divide them up so you have several parcels.) Bake for 1 hour in the preheated oven until the vegetables are tender and slightly caramelized. Cool slightly. Squeeze the garlic out of its skin, peel the other vegetables and cut them into chunks.
3 Meanwhile, in a heavy, non-reactive frying pan, combine the remaining ingredients except the Parmesan cheese and skimmed milk. Cover and boil for 5-7 minutes. Uncover and simmer until the onion is tender, and the liquid about gone.
4 Combine this mixture with the baked vegetables in a food processor and process to a purée. Season to taste.
5 Spread the mixture into a 11 × 7 inches/28 × 18 cm dish or two smaller dishes. Sprinkle with Parmesan cheese, then pour a thin drizzle of milk evenly over the top of the gratin.
6 Bake for 45-55 minutes until bubbly, puffy and browned on the top.

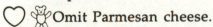Omit Parmesan cheese.

'National cookery is, to a certain extent, governed by a state of mind, and the success with which you will be able to present a typically "Italian" meal rests not so much on your skill in the kitchen as on an instinctive feeling for the underlying taste (both aesthetic and gastronomic) of the country. Therefore, one can in theory prepare a Chinese dinner that is basically Italian in concept, and vice-versa.'

Luigi Carnacina, *Great Italian Cooking*

Salad

'To speak of salads in aught but the most reverential spirit were sacrilege. To be honoured aright, they should be eaten only in the company of the devout or in complete solitude — and perhaps this latter is the wiser plan.'

Elizabeth Robins Pennell, *The Delights of Delicate Eating*

TUNA BEAN SALAD

Tuna bean salad is a store cupboard delight: tinned tuna, tinned beans, a few olives, a scattering of capers . . . If you have no fresh herbs (although fresh parsley and mint are easily available all through the year), do not substitute dried. This is a classic Italian combination (except I've replaced the olive oil with an olive infusion); it never fails to delight people tasting it for the first time.

10 spring onions, trimmed and sliced thin	1 tin (14 oz/400 g) cannellini beans, drained
4 olives, sliced off their stones	2 tablespoons balsamic vinegar
4 sun-dried tomatoes, snipped (use scissors) — optional	1 tablespoon capers, chopped
1 clove garlic, crushed	1 teaspoon of the caper brine
Pinch crushed dried chillies	½ tablespoon lemon juice
½ pt/300 ml stock	1-2 tablespoons shredded fresh mint
1 tin (7 oz/200 g) tuna, drained	1 tablespoon chopped fresh parsley

1   Combine the onion, olives, sun-dried tomatoes, garlic, chillies and the stock in a non-reactive frying pan, cover and boil for 5-7 minutes. Uncover and simmer until the onions are tender, and the liquid is almost gone.
2   Combine with the remaining ingredients and mix thoroughly.

♡ Omit olives.

 ## TOMATO-PEACH SALAD

Years ago, on a scorching, steaming day (as only Atlanta summer days can be), I stopped by to see an Italian friend. I was hungry. I was thirsty. I was hot and bothered and irritable. My friend sat me down with a glass of wine into which he sliced some of the ripest, sweetest peaches (plucked from his tree) I had ever encountered. He went into the garden and picked some tomatoes and a handful of basil. The tomatoes (oh! they were ripe and juicy) were sliced, scattered with the shredded basil and set before me. Never has a meal been so perfect, so delicious, so *restorative*. Ever since then, I think about tomatoes and peaches as natural partners. The logical thing, given the perfection of that therapeutic, simple meal, is to pair them in a salad. You need perfect ingredients. Home-grown tomatoes, bursting with juice and flavour (and *never* stored in the refrigerator), silken Italian peaches (you'll find them in the supermarkets in summertime), fresh basil, and just a sprinkling of balsamic vinegar. Freshly ground pepper brings out all the sweet, ripe flavour. If you grow your own tomatoes, perhaps you grow your own courgettes as well. Serve courgettes with their stuffed blossoms (page 57), followed by this salad. For dessert have Deep Chocolate Sorbet (page 149) with Cherry Compôte (page 133). Can you visualize the intensity of such an experience? Just watch out for sensory overload.

Ripe tomatoes	Freshly ground pepper to taste
Ripe peaches	Balsamic vinegar
Basil or mint leaves	

1   Cut the stem end out of the tomatoes and slice them.
2   Halve the peaches and remove the stone (work over a bowl to catch the juices). Slice the peach halves the same thickness as the tomato slices.
3   Overlap the peach and tomato slices on a pretty plate. Stack

76

the basil or mint leaves, roll the stack, and shred with scissors. Scatter the shreds over the fruit. Grind some pepper over them, and sprinkle with balsamic vinegar, and the reserved peach juices. Serve at once.

ROASTED PEPPER, TOMATO AND MOZZARELLA CHEESE SALAD

I hate the look of food that has been over arranged, over garnished and *fussed* with. Meticulously and artfully arranged ingredients that have the chef's fingerprints all over them (do we *eat* such a plate of food, or lacquer it up and hang it on the wall?), tomato-skin flowers, radish roses, clumps of carefully placed parsley, chive blades that have been tied into *knots*, for heaven's sake, all oh-so-carefully placed just so: it drives me mad. Food is so compellingly beautiful as it is — fussing just ruins it. This salad for instance: snowy slices of moist mozzarella, scarlet-ripe slices of summer tomatoes, vivid yellow grilled pepper halves with a few charred bits still clinging here and there: all you need to do with this bounty is to overlap them on a pretty plate. Don't fuss with the ingredients — they will practically arrange themselves. This dish is rustic and sensually engaging, like a beautiful piece of folk art. And when you have finished admiring it, you can *eat* it — and its tastes are so direct, so unmuddled, so — (what else?) downright *delicious*.

Large ripe tomatoes	*Grilled yellow pepper halves*
Italian-style medium-fat	*(see page 46)*
mozzarella cheese, drained	*Freshly ground pepper*
and blotted dry on a paper	*Balsamic vinegar*
towel	*Lemon juice*

1 Cut the stem end out of the tomatoes and slice the tomatoes. Slice the mozzarella cheese.
2 Alternate tomato slices, cheese slices and pepper halves on a pretty plate. Grind some pepper over them. Sprinkle with a bit of balsamic vinegar and lemon juice.

♡ Omit mozzarella cheese, or use rendered mozzarella cheese (page 8).

OLIVE-CHERRY TOMATO SALAD

Makes 2 pts/1.1 l

The sight of olive salad, glistening black and green and herb-flecked in huge pottery bowls, is one of my earliest and most vivid memories of Italian food. I've added quartered cherry tomatoes, reduced the amount of olives, and generally lightened the classic. It's fresh tasting, exuberantly colourful and − in my opinion − even more delicious than the original.

---

18 oz/500 g firm, ripe cherry tomatoes, stemmed and quartered (use half red, half yellow cherry tomatoes if available)	*1-3 cloves garlic, crushed (the amount depends on your taste)*
5 green olives, sliced off the stones into slivers	*Juice of ½ lemon*
5 black olives, sliced off the stones into slivers	*3 spring onions, trimmed and sliced thin*
2 teaspoons of the olive brine	*2 tablespoons chopped fresh parsley (flat leaf if possible)*
1 chilli pepper, minced	*2 tablespoons shredded fresh mint or basil*
1½ tablespoons capers	*Freshly ground pepper to taste*
1½ tablespoons balsamic vinegar	

---

1 Combine all ingredients. Let stand at room temperature until serving time. (Stir it up occasionally.) To keep for more than a few hours, store in the refrigerator.

MUFFULETTA

In New Orleans there was (probably still is, for that matter) a wonderful, several-generations-old Italian food shop called The Central Grocery. One of the specialities of The Central Grocery was an astounding sandwich: the Muffuletta. It consisted of a huge round Italian roll filled with sliced Italian cold cuts and smothered with a lavish amount of olive salad. Standard procedure in New Orleans was to purchase one of these monsters at the Grocery, and then to wander − dripping and munching − over to the railroad tracks, there to contemplate the great complexities of life while gazing at the Mississippi and engulfing every last crumb of sandwich. Here is the Slim Cuisine version. I can't supply the murky, rushing river, but all the olive-rich, herby, smoky taste is there.

Focaccia or Ballooned Sandwich Rolls (page 123)	*Thinly sliced Parma ham, trimmed of fat*
Thinly sliced smoked turkey breast	*Olive-Cherry Tomato Salad (see page 78)*

1   Split the bread. Lay a few slices of turkey and ham on the bottom. Put a lavish layer of Olive-Cherry Tomato Salad over the meat. Press down on the top half of the bread.
2   Wrap and weight (with a brick, or heavy tinned goods) for an hour or so. (This is optional, only if you have the time.)

 ## BEETROOT-ROCKET SALAD

Makes approximately 1 pt/570 ml

The bitterness of rocket against the sweetness of beetroot make a stunning contrast. The green against the red is pretty stunning, too. This is another one of those simple salads that practically arranges itself.

3-4 baked, peeled beetroots (see page 45)	*1 tablespoon balsamic vinegar*
	Juice of ½ lemon
3 black olives in brine, drained and sliced off the stone	*Freshly ground pepper to taste*
	Rocket leaves (if you can't find rocket use spinach leaves)
1 teaspoon olive brine	
1 tablespoon beetroot juices	

1   Slice the beetroot and arrange the slices, overlapped in rows, on a pretty white or clear glass platter. Scatter the olive slivers over them.
2   Combine the brine, beetroot juice, vinegar and lemon juice, and pour the liquid over the slices. Grind on some pepper. Surround the slices decoratively with rocket leaves.

♡ 🧸 Omit olives.

🕐 Use vacuum-packed (no vinegar), ready cooked beetroot.

BEETROOT-ORANGE SALAD

Red exhilarates me, and makes me feel younger, more attractive and livelier. It's no wonder that I find this combination quite irresistible. Believe it or not, I serve this salad on ruby glass plates, but you might try clear glass or white china.

2 large baked beetroots (see page 45)	*2 tablespoons shredded basil*
3 blood oranges	*2 tablespoons chopped parsley*
Juice of 1 lemon	*½ tablespoon snipped chives*
1 tablespoon balsamic vinegar	*Freshly ground pepper*

1 Peel and coarsely dice the beetroot and place in a bowl.
2 Peel two oranges of all peel and pith, section them, and cut each section in half. Add to the beetroot. Squeeze the juice of the remaining orange over the contents of the bowl.
3 Combine the remaining ingredients and toss them with the beetroot-orange mixture.

Use vacuum-packed (no vinegar), ready cooked beetroot.

Pasta, Polenta and Rice

'Please don't cut your spaghetti when it is served to you.
This is some kind of a sin for which I have no name, only
a great conviction.'

Edwin H. Knopf, *The Food of Italy*

Pasta

I travel the country, lecturing and demonstrating Slim Cuisine. During the question and answer period someone *always* asks the inevitable question: 'What do you *really* eat? What do you feed your family, what do you cook for dinner every night?' The answer is simple — in fact it's one word: 'Pasta.' My husband and son love it as much as I do — pasta is the meal we choose when we need comfort, when we want to celebrate, when we just feel the need for something lavish, delicious and exciting. There are so many possible ways of serving pasta that you could have it every night for a year and never repeat yourself. Best of all, pasta is *quick*. Put up the water in a big pot. While it comes to the boil, and then while the pasta cooks, the sauce can be made, the salad tossed, the table set, and the family gathered into the by-now aromatic kitchen. And pasta — with Slim Cuisine sauces — can make an extremely nutritious and complete meal.

Pasta Guidelines

Italian-made packaged dry pasta (made from durum wheat

semolina) is available in all large supermarkets in all sizes and shapes, and it is an excellent product. It's also very simple to cook.

1 Bring plenty of lightly salted water to a rolling boil; at least 5 pts/2.8 l of water per pound/450 g of pasta. If you are stingy with the water, the pasta will be gummy. Instead of salting the water, you can add a few teaspoons of brine from a jar of olives. The brine will salt the water and will also add a subtle olive taste.

2 When the water is violently boiling, add the pasta, stirring with a wooden spoon as you do so. Long pasta such as spaghetti, linguine, etc., should be separated with the spoon as it begins to cook.

3 Stir frequently as it boils so that the pieces do not clump together. *Never* put the lid on the pot!

4 Do not overcook your pasta or you will end up with mush. Cook it until it is *al dente* (to the tooth). In other words, the pasta should be slightly resistant to the bite − not at all raw, of course, but not at all mushy either. Begin fishing out pieces to taste − test early enough to avoid overcooking. (Use the timing suggested on the package as a guideline only.)

5 Have a large colander waiting in the sink. When the pasta is *just* done, don't dawdle. Use oven gloves and extreme care. Drain it quickly into the colander, combine it with its sauce, and serve *at once*. (Cooked *pasta* does not freeze well, but most of the *sauces* in the following chapter freeze beautifully.)

PASTA WITH GARLIC, SUN-DRIED TOMATOES AND SMOKED CHICKEN

Makes 1¼ pts/700 ml of sauce (will sauce approximately 1 lb/450 g of pasta)

Nuggets of smoked chicken (or smoked turkey) breast along with mushrooms and peppers, the Slim Cuisine Italian infusion, and a touch of tomato purée, make a pleasing smoky, spicy sauce for pasta. I also like this sauce with slices of plain polenta, or Broccoli Polenta (page 104).

3 large cloves of garlic, crushed	into large squares
1 pt/570 ml stock	6 oz/175 g button mushrooms,
4 fl oz/110 ml dry white	quartered
vermouth	2 tablespoons tomato purée
3-4 sun-dried tomatoes, snipped	Freshly ground pepper to taste
(use scissors) — optional	½ lb/225 g smoked chicken or
6-7 black olives in brine, drained	turkey, diced
and sliced off the stones	3-4 tablespoons grated
Pinch or 2 crushed dried chillies	Parmesan cheese
1 yellow and 1 red pepper,	1 lb/450 g pasta, freshly cooked
cored, seeded, peeled and cut	and drained

1 Combine garlic, half of the stock, the vermouth, sun-dried tomatoes, olives and chillies in a heavy-bottomed frying pan. Boil, uncovered, stirring occasionally, until the garlic is tender and the liquid is reduced to about half.

2 Stir in the peppers. Cook on a moderate heat, stirring, until they are almost tender.

3 Add the mushrooms. Add a bit of stock if needed. Cook, stirring occasionally, until the mushrooms are tender. Add the remaining stock. Boil until reduced by half. Stir in the tomato purée. Cook for a few more minutes. Season with pepper. Add the diced chicken.

4 Toss the sauce and the Parmesan cheese with 1 lb/450 g of freshly cooked pasta shells or pasta shapes.

♡ Omit olives and cheese.

❄ The sauce freezes well.

 # PASTA WITH CAULIFLOWER

Makes 1½ pts/900 ml sauce (will sauce 1 lb/450 g pasta)

This is a purely vegetarian version of the previous recipe with cubes of potato and florets of cauliflower added to the infusion, peppers and tomato purée of the basic sauce. The sauce calls for a sturdy pasta shape: penne (pasta quills) are perfect.

6-7 sun-dried tomatoes, snipped (use scissors) — optional	1 head cauliflower, trimmed and broken into florets
4-5 black olives, sliced off the stone	1 small baking potato, cut into 1½ inch/3.5-cm cubes
2 cloves garlic, crushed	Salt and freshly ground pepper to taste
A generous pinch or two of crushed dried chillies	2-3 tablespoons shredded fresh basil leaves
1 pt/570 ml stock	2-3 tablespoons tomato purée
4-5 fl oz/110-150 ml dry white vermouth	1 lb/450 g pasta quills (penne), freshly cooked and drained
1 red and 1 yellow pepper peeled and cut into 2-inch/5-cm pieces	

1   Combine the sun-dried tomatoes, olives, garlic, chillies, half the stock and the vermouth in a large, non-reactive heavy frying pan or wok. Bring to the boil. Boil uncovered for 5-7 minutes. Toss in the peppers, cauliflower and potato. Add the remaining stock and season with salt and pepper. Cover and simmer for approximately 15 minutes, uncovering occasionally to stir, until the cauliflower and potato are almost tender.

2   Stir in the basil, tomato purée and a bit of water or additional stock if the liquid has cooked down too much (the mixture should be soupy, not dry). Cook, uncovered, stirring occasionally, until the vegetables are tender. Serve tossed with penne.

♡ Omit olives.

❄ The sauce freezes well.

♡❄ PASTA WITH RED PEPPER SAUCE

Makes approximately 2 pts/1.1 l sauce (will generously sauce 1 lb 2 oz/500 g pasta)

Red peppers (and yellow ones too) are my pet vegetables. You can do so much with them! They look so good, they are so sweet and — when peeled — they cook to such a buttery texture. And, best of all, when sautéed in stock, they form a syrupy, thick sauce that coats pasta extremely well. *But* — you must peel them before cooking. Yes, I know it's a nuisance, but *it's worth it*! Toss this sauce into pasta shells or other shapes that have cavities or depressions, so that bits of the peppers and herbs get caught in the depressions, and the buttery sauce coats each nook and cranny.

---

10 red peppers or red/yellow mixed, peeled and cut into squares	12 fl oz/350 ml stock
	1 lb/450 g pasta shapes
	15 basil leaves (shredded)
2 fresh chillies, finely chopped	1 tablespoon chopped parsley
4 cloves garlic, coarsely chopped	

---

1 Combine the peppers, chillies, garlic and stock in a heavy-bottomed frying pan, and cook, stirring occasionally, until the peppers are tender and syrupy.
2 Cook the pasta (shells, penne, or other shapes), drain and combine with the sauce.
3 Toss in the basil leaves and parsley. Serve at once.

❄ The sauce freezes well.

⏲🥕 PASTA WITH FENNEL AND PEPPERS

Makes 3 pts/1.7 l pasta and sauce

Cook strips of fennel, strips of pepper and cloves of garlic in the same water that the pasta will be cooked in, then use some of that water to make an onion-olive infusion. When the pasta is cooked, toss it with the vegetables, the infusion and some grated cheese. This is easy, the clean-up is minimal and the dish makes a wonderfully satisfying pasta supper.

---

2 heads fennel, trimmed and cut lengthwise into quarters	4 spring onions, trimmed and sliced thin
2-3 cloves whole garlic (optional)	2 cloves garlic, crushed
2 peppers, seeded, cored, peeled and cut into 1-inch/2.5-cm wide strips	4 olives in brine, drained and sliced off their stones
	2-3 tablespoons grated Parmesan cheese
12 oz/350 g pasta quills (penne)	

---

1 Boil up a large pot of lightly salted water. Put the fennel and garlic into the boiling water and cook for 6 minutes. Then add the peppers and cook for a further 7 minutes. Then remove all the vegetables with a slotted spoon or a skimmer and let drain in a colander.

2   Put the pasta into the water and cook, stirring occasionally, until *al dente*.
3   While the pasta is cooking, ladle out ½ pt/300 ml of the pasta water and combine in a frying pan with the spring onions, crushed garlic and the olives. Simmer, until the onions are tender and the liquid about gone.
4   Drain the pasta (save some of the water), mix with the vegetables and the infusion. Stir in 2-3 tablespoons of the cooking water. Sprinkle on the Parmesan cheese, toss together and serve at once.

♡ Omit olives and cheese.

 ## PASTA WITH SPRING ONIONS, PEAS AND OLIVES

Makes 1½ pts/900 ml sauce (will sauce ¾ lb/350 g pasta)

Vibrant, summery and absolutely beautiful to look at, this delicate, green-and-white pasta dish is a seasonal treat. If there is any leftover use it to fill a Frittata (page 51).

25 thin spring onions, trimmed and sliced thin	1 lb/450 g very fresh peas, or ¾ lb/350 g frozen peas, thawed
2-3 cloves garlic, minced	
4-5 black olives in brine, drained and sliced off the stone	3 tablespoons shredded fresh mint leaves
1 teaspoon olive brine	Freshly ground pepper
Juice of 1 lemon	½-¾ lb/225/350 g pasta
1 pt/570 ml stock	corkscrews, freshly cooked and drained

1   Combine the sliced onions, garlic, olives, olive brine, half the lemon juice and half of the stock. Cover and boil for 5-7 minutes. Uncover and simmer until the onions and garlic are tender and the liquid is almost gone.
2   Add the peas, remaining lemon juice and remaining stock. Simmer until the peas are just tender. Stir in the mint and season with pepper. Toss the sauce with the cooked pasta.

♡ Omit olives.

Pasta – the ultimate in Italian comfort: anticlockwise from the
foreground: penne primavera; pasta shells with red pepper sauce;
linguine with ricotta pesto.

Sustaining sandwiches on country bread: clockwise from the foreground: muffuletta (smoked turkey, Parma ham and olive-cherry tomato salad); grilled mushroom; sausages and pepper; caponata.

PASTA PRIMAVERA

Makes 1½ pts/900 ml pasta and sauce

Just as Spaghetti Bolognese has become a sort of generic term for pasta with a variety of meat sauces, so has Pasta Primavera come to mean pasta with a seasonal vegetable sauce. The original Italian Pasta Primavera referred to thin spaghetti tossed with the first tomatoes of the season, along with some herbs and olive oil, but now it can refer to any number of variations featuring fresh vegetables along with the tomatoes and herbs.

6 oz/175 g button mushrooms, quartered	*1 medium courgette trimmed and sliced about ½-inch/1-cm thick*
1 bunch spring onions, trimmed and sliced thin	*4 fresh, ripe tomatoes, cored, skinned, seeded and coarsely diced*
1 clove garlic, minced	
8 fl oz/225 ml stock	
1 red and 1 yellow pepper cut into their natural sections, peeled, and then cut into 1-inch/2.5-cm squares	*4-5 leaves of basil, shredded*
	Salt and freshly ground pepper
	3-4 tablespoons grated Parmesan cheese
1 head fennel, trimmed, cut in half lengthways, and sliced	*Approximately ½ lb/225 g pasta (penne)*

1 In a big pot, heat the water for the pasta.
2 Combine the mushrooms, spring onions, garlic and about 5 fl oz/150 ml of stock in a flame-proof casserole. Simmer until the vegetables are tender and most of the liquid has cooked away.
3 Meanwhile, peel and slice the peppers, and trim and slice the fennel and courgette.
4 Add the peppers to the mushroom mix along with another few fluid ounces of stock. Cook, stirring occasionally, until the peppers are almost tender. Add the fennel and courgette – cook and stir a few minutes more, until all the vegetables are tender.
5 Meanwhile, put the whole tomatoes in a sieve and dip them into the boiling pasta water for 10 seconds. Refresh briefly under cold water. Core, skin and seed the tomatoes, and then dice them roughly. Add to the vegetables along with the shredded basil. Season with salt and pepper. Let the mixture cook gently, while the pasta cooks.
6 The sauce is ready when the tomatoes have lost their shape

and the mixture is thick and savoury. When the pasta is *al dente*, drain it and toss it with the sauce directly in the casserole.

♡ Omit Parmesan cheese.

❄ The sauce freezes well.

♡⊕🥕 RAW TOMATO SAUCE FOR PASTA

Makes 1¼ pts/700 ml (will sauce ¾ lb/350 g pasta)

There are few gastronomic experiences equal to eating steaming hot pasta with an icy cold, fresh tomato sauce. It's the 'hot as summer, cold as winter' effect that will send frissons of pleasure up and down your spine. The tomatoes must be *real* tomatoes — juicy ripe and scarlet red — and the herbs must be fresh.

3 lbs/1.4 kg ripe tomatoes, peeled, seeded and chopped	*2 teaspoons chopped fresh oregano leaves*
1 clove garlic, minced (optional)	*2 tablespoons chopped fresh parsley (flat leaf if available)*
3 spring onions, trimmed — mince the white portion, thinly slice the green	*2 tablespoons balsamic vinegar*
	Juice of 1 lemon
4 tablespoons shredded mint leaves	*1 tablespoon drained capers*
	1 teaspoon caper brine
4 tablespoons shredded basil leaves	*¾ lb/350 g pasta*
	Freshly ground pepper to taste

1   Combine all the ingredients except the pasta and pepper. Chill well. (Fast chill, if necessary, by putting it into the freezer while the pasta cooks.)
2   Cook ¾ lb/350 g small pasta (shells, corkscrews, etc.), or linguine until *al dente*. Drain and immediately toss with the chilled mixture. Grind on some pepper. Serve *at once*.

♡ *Variation* Toss diced grilled red and yellow peppers (page 46) with their juices into the tomato sauce.

⊕🥕 RAW VEGETABLE SAUCE FOR PASTA

Makes 3 pts/1.7 l sauce (will generously sauce 18 oz/500 g pasta)

This chilled vegetable, hot pasta combo will knock your socks off.

The sauce is an amalgamation of colourful diced vegetables in herbed tomato juice that has been enlivened with hot pepper sauce, balsamic vinegar and citrus juices: lavish it over hot pasta shapes and serve it as the star of a gala summertime buffet.

3 peppers (1 green, 1 red, 1 yellow), cored, seeded, peeled and finely diced	5 black olives in brine, drained and sliced off the stone
4 ripe tomatoes, peeled, seeded, juiced and diced	1 tablespoon capers
1 small head fennel, trimmed and finely diced	4-5 tablespoons mixed shredded fresh basil and mint leaves
5 spring onions, trimmed — the white part diced, the green part thinly sliced	2-3 tablespoons chopped fresh parsley (flat leaf if available)
4-5 small courgettes, trimmed and finely diced	8 fl oz/225 ml tomato juice
½ small cucumber, peeled, halved lengthwise, seeded and finely diced	Several dashes Tabasco sauce
	1 tablespoon olive brine
	1 tablespoon caper brine
	3 tablespoons balsamic vinegar
	Juice of 1 large orange
2 carrots, peeled and diced	Juice of ½ large lemon
5 green olives in brine, drained and sliced off the stone	Freshly ground pepper
	1 lb 2 oz/500 g pasta shapes (corkscrews, shells, bow ties, etc.)

1 Combine the vegetables, olives, capers and herbs.
2 Mix together the tomato juice, Tabasco, olive brine, caper brine, balsamic vinegar, orange juice, lemon juice and pepper.
3 Toss the tomato juice mixture into the vegetables. Chill.
4 Cook 1 lb 2 oz/500 g small pasta (shells, rotini, or the like) until *al dente*. Drain. Toss together the steaming hot pasta and chilled vegetables. Serve at once.

♡ Omit olives.

CREAMY PASTA

Makes 2 pts/1.1 l pasta with sauce

This recipe was inspired by memories of Pasta Alfredo, that outrageously rich pasta dish achieved by tossing freshly cooked *al dente* fettuccini (pasta ribbons) with quantities of double cream, butter and grated Parmesan cheese. I first had this seductive dish in New York at Leone's Italian restaurant in the

Fifties, before Leone's (supposedly, in its heyday, Caruso's favourite restaurant when he was performing in New York) was taken over by a huge restaurant conglomerate. Gene Leone, it seemed, learned to make the dish from the master himself, so even though Fettucine Alfredo in New York wasn't quite the same as having it in Rome served directly from Alfredo's famous gold fork and spoon, it was close enough to be pretty exciting to a hungry teenager, whose gastronomic awareness was just beginning to develop. I still think that fettuccini tossed with a creamy, cheesy sauce makes a spectacularly comforting meal, but many other things have changed. In the thirty plus years that have passed since those days, I've been through years of obesity (the result of that pasta dish, and countless other classic high-fat dishes that encompass The World of Cuisine), I've been through a substantial weight loss, and, finally, I've come to recognize the dangers − in relation to weight maintenance *and* to health − of a high-fat diet. Thus this recipe − Fettuccini *not* Alfredo − bathes the pasta in a sauce that is seductively creamy, deliciously cheesy, ineffably comforting − and drastically fat reduced.

10 oz/275 g fettuccini, tagliatelle or linguine	room temperature
8 oz/225 g quark, at room temperature	3 tablespoons freshly grated Parmesan cheese
3 fl oz/75 ml skimmed milk, at	Freshly ground pepper to taste

1   Cook pasta to the *al dente* stage.
2   Meanwhile, put the quark into a large, warm bowl. With a wooden spoon, thoroughly stir in the skimmed milk and grated cheese.
3   Drain the pasta and immediately toss it into the quark mixture. Grind in some pepper if desired, and serve at once.

Variation:

CREAMY PASTA WITH TOMATO SAUCE

Prepare the above recipe. Top each serving with a dollop of Quick Tomato Sauce with Capers (page 109).

'I can still see his (Alfredo's) beaming face as he
recognised and welcomed me. He would shout, with all
the gestures of a true Roman, "*Ecco il mio caro amico,
Eugenio Leone di New York. E stato lui che mi ha insegnato il*

mio buon mestiere." (Here is my dear friend Gene Leone of
New York. It is he who taught me my wonderful trade.)
Even though it wasn't true at all, it sounded awfully
good, especially when I was entertaining friends.'

Gene Leone, *Leone's Italian Cookbook*

PASTA BOW-TIES WITH
NEW POTATOES AND MINT

Makes 1 pt/570 ml sauce (will sauce 12 oz/350 g pasta bow-ties)

Pasta and potatoes combined in one dish occur often in Italian
cuisine. Here, halves of tiny new potatoes, and bow-tie noodles
(*farfalle*) cohabit in a herb − and chilli − brightened tomato
sauce. The two starches are brilliant together and provide enough
complex carbohydrate to gladden the heart of any modern-day,
nutrition-conscious food lover.

4 black olives in brine, drained and sliced off the stones	1 tin (14 oz/400 g) chopped tomatoes, whirled in the liquidizer until smooth
4-5 sun-dried tomatoes, snipped (use scissors) − optional	Freshly ground pepper to taste
3 cloves garlic, minced	1 tablespoon tomato purée
1 onion, chopped	2 tablespoons chopped fresh parsley
Pinch or two of crushed dried chillies	2 tablespoons shredded fresh mint
10 tiny new potatoes, halved	12 oz/350 g pasta bow-ties, cooked, and drained
½ pt/300 ml stock	

1   Combine the olives, tomatoes, garlic, onion, chillies, potatoes
    and stock in a heavy non-reactive frying pan. Cover and boil
    for 7-10 minutes. Uncover and simmer briskly stirring occa-
    sionally, until the onions and potatoes are frying in their own
    juices, and the onions are tender.
2   Pour in the tomatoes and season to taste with freshly ground
    pepper. Simmer for approximately 10 minutes. Stir in the
    tomato purée and simmer for 5 minutes more. Stir in the
    herbs. Serve tossed into freshly cooked and drained bow-tie
    pasta.

♡ Omit the olives.

✸ MEAT-FILLED CANNELLONI

Cannelloni are filled pasta rolls, served in a sauce that complements the filling. Fresh pasta (lasagne) sheets are available from speciality shops and Italian delis, and from the chill cabinets of major supermarkets. If the sheets are too big, cut them down to size. This recipe is a blueprint: make as many as you need.

Fresh lasagne sheets, approximately 5 in × 6 in/ 12.5 × 15 cm	Tomato Sauce (page 107) or Quick Tomato Sauce with Capers (page 109)
Stracotto (page 34)	Grated Parmesan cheese

1 Preheat oven to 350°F, 180°C, Gas Mark 4.
2 Prepare the lasagne sheets according to package directions, but undercook them somewhat. Drain, spread out on tea towels and blot dry. Spread a thin layer of tomato sauce in the bottom of a shallow baking dish or gratin dish.
3 Spoon a generous tablespoon of Stracotto along each sheet, and roll. Put each sheet, seam side down in the baking dish. They should be in a single layer.
4 Spread sauce over the pasta rolls. Sprinkle with Parmesan. Bake for 15 minutes covered, then approximately 10 minutes uncovered. Serve at once.

Variation

CANNELLONI FILLED WITH MEAT AND CHEESE

When you fill the pasta sheets, put a thin strip of mozzarella cheese on the meat filling before rolling.

✸ MUSHROOM CANNELLONI

Makes 8 pieces

This beautiful vegetarian dish is imbued with the lovely flavour and aroma of mushrooms. The porcini mushrooms in the Intense Mushroom Pâté (page 115) give it its soul. Have all the ingredients warmed before you begin to put it together; then it needs only a brief stay in the oven. Overcooking will ruin the exquisite delicacy of the cannelloni.

Sauce

½ pt/300 ml stock	4 black olives in brine, sliced off
⅕ pt/110 ml mushroom-soaking	their stones
liquid (see page 5)	2 cloves garlic, chopped
⅕ pt/110 ml dry white	4 heaped tablespoons Intense
vermouth	Mushroom Pâté (page 115)
	½ pt/300 ml tomato passato

Cannelloni

8 fresh lasagne sheets	8 rounded tablespoons shredded
Approximately 16 rounded	mozzarella cheese
tablespoons Intense	5 tablespoons grated Parmesan
Mushroom Pâté (page 115)	cheese

1   To make the sauce: in a heavy-bottomed frying pan, combine the stock, mushroom-soaking liquid and vermouth. (If you have no mushroom-soaking liquid on hand, use more stock.) Bring to the boil and boil until reduced by almost half. Throw in the olives and garlic, cover and boil for approximately 5 minutes. Uncover and simmer until the garlic pieces are tender and the liquid is almost gone. Stir in the Intense Mushroom Pâté and the tomato Passato and simmer for 2-3 minutes. Set aside.

2   Prepare the lasagne sheets according to package directions, but undercook them slightly. Drain, rinse and drain again.

3   Lay out the lasagne sheets on a tea towel and blot dry. Put 2 tablespoons of Intense Mushroom Pâté on each sheet. Top with 1 tablespoon mozzarella cheese and 1 teaspoon grated Parmesan cheese. Roll each lasagne sheet into a tube and put it, seam side down, in a baking dish that can hold all the rolls in one layer. Spread the sauce over the pasta rolls and sprinkle with the remaining grated Parmesan cheese. Cover. Bake at 350°F, 180°C, Gas Mark 4 for approximately 15 minutes, covered, and 5-7 minutes uncovered, until warmed through. Serve at once.

♡Omit cheeses and olives.

❄ CHEESE-FILLED CANNELLONI WITH MEAT SAUCE

Makes 12 rolls

I've been making this hearty, family-style dish for years, in fact I printed a very similar recipe in my first book — *The Nutrition Cookbook* — in the Seventies. The delicacy of the cheese filling is somewhat overwhelmed by the rambunctious meat sauce: one is left with an impression of pleasing creaminess in the centre of the dish. I feel that family meals often call for just this sort of over-the-top heartiness. But if you wish to emphasize the delicacy, substitute a tomato sauce (see the sauce chapter) for the meat sauce.

¼ lb/110 g quark	2 egg whites, beaten to firm
¼ lb/110 g low-fat or medium-	peaks
fat ricotta cheese	12 lasagne sheets, cooked
½ lb/225 g Italian-style	(undercook slightly)
mozzarella cheese, drained,	according to package
blotted dry on paper towels,	directions, spread out and
and shredded	blotted dry
¼ teaspoon freshly grated	Bolognese sauce (page 114) or
nutmeg	Sausage sauce (page 113)
Salt and freshly ground pepper	2 tablespoons grated Parmesan
to taste	cheese

1 Combine the quark, ricotta, mozzarella, nutmeg, salt and pepper in the food processor container. Process until well amalgamated. Transfer to a bowl. Stir in one quarter of the beaten egg whites, fold in the remainder.
2 Divide the mixture among the 12 lasagne sheets and roll each sheet.
3 Put a thin layer of the meat sauce in a shallow baking dish that will hold the pasta rolls in one layer. Arrange the rolls seam side down, over the sauce. Top with the remaining sauce and sprinkle with the grated cheese. Cover with foil.
4 Bake in a 350°F, 180°C, Gas Mark 4 oven for 20-25 minutes. Uncover and bake for 5-10 minutes more.

🥕 Instead of Meat Sauce, use Tomato Sauce.

✳🥕CANNELLONI WITH RICOTTA PESTO

Makes 12 rolls

Ricotta pesto combines the vivid basil taste of pesto sauce with the creaminess of ricotta cheese. If you wrap that splendour in perfectly cooked sheets of fresh pasta, blanket it with home-made tomato sauce, and quickly bake it under a light mantle of grated Parmesan cheese you have a wondrous dish indeed. Cut into one of the pasta rolls with the side of your fork, watch the creamy pesto ooze out to meld with the tomato sauce . . . I'm getting carried away, but when you taste it, you'll know why.

12 fresh lasagne sheets, cooked (undercook slightly) according to package directions, spread out and blotted dry	*1 recipe Ricotta Pesto (page 116) 1 recipe warm Tomato Sauce (page 107) 1-2 tablespoons grated Parmesan cheese*

1 Fill each lasagne sheet with a tablespoon of ricotta pesto and roll (see page 93).
2 Film a shallow baking dish (that can hold the pasta rolls in one layer) with a thin layer of tomato sauce. Arrange the rolls seam side down over the sauce. Cover with the remaining sauce. Sprinkle with Parmesan cheese. Cover the baking dish.
3 Bake at 350°F, 180°C, Gas Mark 4, covered, for 10-15 minutes until heated through.

 ## SPINACH CANNELLONI

Makes 12 rolls

A mixture of spinach, mozzarella cheese and quark, lightened by beaten egg whites and flavoured with a dusting of freshly grated nutmeg makes a fresh tasting pasta filling. Again, tomato sauce makes a perfect topping; pick the one you like best from the sauce chapter.

1 small (7 oz/200 g) carton quark	spinach
4 oz/110 g Italian-style medium-fat mozzarella cheese, drained, blotted dry on paper towels, and shredded	2 egg whites, beaten to firm peaks
	12 fresh lasagne sheets cooked (undercook slightly) according to package directions, spread out and blotted dry
¼ teaspoon freshly grated nutmeg	
Salt and freshly ground pepper to taste	
	Warm Tomato Sauce (page 107)
8 fl oz/225 g defrosted and squeezed dry, frozen chopped	2 tablespoons grated Parmesan cheese

1 Preheat the oven to 350°F, 180°C, Gas Mark 4.
2 Combine the quark, mozzarella cheese, nutmeg, salt, pepper and spinach in the food processor. Pulse the processor on and off until the mixture forms a rough purée. Don't make it too smooth. Scrape into a bowl. Stir ¼ of the egg whites into the mixture to lighten it. Fold in the remainder.
3 Divide the mixture among the 12 lasagne sheets and roll each sheet.
4 Spread a thin layer of sauce in a shallow baking dish that will hold all the rolls in one layer. Put the rolls in the dish, seam side down, in one layer. Top with the remaining sauce and sprinkle with cheese.
5 Bake covered for 15 minutes. Uncover and bake for 7-10 minutes longer.

 # AUBERGINE LASAGNE

Lasagne — layered casseroles of pasta sheets, savoury sauces (often a tomato or meat sauce *and* a cream sauce), cheeses and (sometimes) vegetables — have many, many variations. My luscious but low-fat versions contain a layer of quark (or quark combined with low-fat ricotta) that has been mixed with mozzarella and lightened with beaten egg whites. As a result, these lasagne have a voluptuously smooth and rich creamy layer that — although low in fat — deliver the taste and texture satisfaction of the killer, high-fat traditional lasagne. In this version, grilled aubergine slices are slipped in between the pasta, tomato sauce and cheese layers. The final resting time, between oven and eating, is important; without it, it would be impossible to cut the lasagne into neat squares.

1 lb/450 g quark
½ lb/225 g Italian-style
   mozzarella cheese, drained
   and blotted dry, and shredded
Salt and freshly ground pepper
   to taste
3 egg whites, beaten to firm
   peaks
3-4 aubergines, cut into ¼-½
   inch/0.5-1 cm slices, grilled
   (page 46)

1 pt/570 ml Quick Tomato Sauce
   with Capers (page 109)
6 (5 × 6 inch/12.5 × 15 cm)
   sheets lasagne, cooked
   (undercooked slightly)
   according to package
   directions, spread out and
   blotted dry
4-5 tablespoons Parmesan
   cheese

1   Preheat the oven to 400°F, 200°C, Gas Mark 6.
2   Combine the quark, mozzarella cheese, salt and pepper in the bowl of a food processor. Process until well amalgamated. Transfer to a bowl. Stir in one quarter of the beaten egg whites, fold in the remainder. Cut each aubergine slice in half.
3   Put a thin layer of the tomato sauce into the bottom of a baking dish (12 × 7 inches/30.5 × 18 cm), cover with a layer of 3 sheets of lasagne, then with a layer of overlapping aubergine slices. Spread on the quark-cheese mixture and 2 tablespoons of Parmesan cheese. Top with another layer of aubergine slices, then 3 more sheets of lasagne, top with another layer of aubergines, spread on the remaining tomato sauce and finally sprinkle on the remaining Parmesan cheese.
4   Bake in the oven, covered, for 15 minutes, uncovered for 10-15 minutes. Allow to rest on a rack for 10-15 minutes before serving.

♡Omit mozzarella and Parmesan cheese.

Fresh Lasagne

Fresh lasagne sheets are best in these recipes: they are available from Italian delis and speciality shops, and from the chill cabinets of many major supermarkets. The actual number of sheets you need for each recipe depends on the size of the sheets. If you can't find the fresh pasta, use dried packaged lasagne. Cook it first in boiling water (undercook it), drain well and blot dry before assembling the dish.

❊ MEAT LASAGNE

Stracotto (page 34), that deep-flavoured, long-simmered filling of finely diced veal or pork, forms the meat layer in this festive lasagne; alternately you could use Bolognese Sauce (page 114) or Sausage Sauce (page 113). Each gives its own quality to the lasagne. The Stracotto imparts a deep-roasted meat flavour; the Bolognese Sauce, which contains chopped carrots and peppers, gives a vegetable sweetness, the Sausage Sauce adds spiciness. Each, in its own way, is superb, and should please any meat eater you feed. The vegetarians will love the aubergine lasagne (previous recipe).

½ lb/225 g low-fat or medium-fat ricotta cheese

½ lb/225 g quark

½ lb/225 g Italian-style mozzarella cheese, drained and blotted dry

Salt and freshly ground pepper to taste

3 egg whites, beaten to firm peaks

1 pt/570 ml Quick Tomato Sauce with Capers (page 109)

9 sheets (5 × 6 inches/12.5 × 15 cm) fresh lasagne, cooked (undercook slightly) according to package directions, spread out and blotted dry

1 recipe Stracotto (page 34)

4-5 tablespoons Parmesan cheese

1 Preheat the oven to 400°F, 200°C, Gas Mark 6.
2 Combine the ricotta, quark, mozzarella cheese, salt and pepper in the bowl of a food processor. Process until well amalgamated. Transfer to a bowl. Stir in one quarter of the beaten egg whites, fold in the remainder.
3 Put a thin layer of the tomato sauce on the bottom of a 12 × 7 inch/30.5 × 18 cm baking dish and cover with a layer of lasagne sheets. Spread on an even layer of Stracotto, top with 3 more lasagne sheets. Spread on the cheese mixture, top with 3 more lasagne sheets, and spread on the remaining Stracotto. Top with the last 3 lasagne sheets, spread with tomato sauce, and sprinkle on the grated Parmesan cheese.
4 Bake in the oven, covered, for 15 minutes, and uncovered for 15 minutes. Allow to rest on a rack for 10-15 minutes before serving.

POTATO GNOCCHI

Makes 2½ pts/1.4 l

Gnocchi are adorable little potato dumplings. The gnocchi dough is easily mixed from potatoes and light flour, formed into ropes, cut into one inch/2.5 cm pieces, and then flung into boiling water. When the gnocchi rise to the top (a few minutes is all it takes), they are done. Most of the time, the little dumplings are marked with the tines of a fork to create ridges, but I've also seen them simply dented with a finger, and I prefer them that way — the dented dumplings seem more homespun, somehow. The amount of flour you need will depend on the moisture of the potatoes, and of the flour, not to mention the humidity in the air, so use the recipe as a guide only. The dough should be smooth and soft, with a slight stickiness, but should hold together. Don't be tempted to add too much flour; you want these dumplings to be feather light and delicate. Potato Gnocchi are very easy to make — the best thing is to just get your hands in the dough, and *do it* — it's really quite simple. Serve them as soon as they are done, with any one of the tomato sauces or meat sauces in the meat chapter, or with Beef Rolls in Tomato Sauce (page 21).

---

2 lbs/900 g baking potatoes, boiled in their skins, peeled and pushed through a ricer or a mouli while still warm (makes 1 lb 7 oz/650 g riced potatoes)	Approx 6 oz/175 g light plain flour Salt ¾-1 pt/400-570 ml warm Tomato Sauce (choose the one you like from the sauce chapter)

---

1   Bring a large pot of salted water to the boil. Have ready on your work surface a lightly floured platter.
2   Meanwhile, put the potatoes, most of the flour and salt in a large bowl. With your hands, work it together, until you have a beautifully smooth, slightly sticky dough. Add a bit more flour as necessary. Knead it lightly a few times in the bowl, or on your lightly floured work surface, but don't over-knead or the gnocchi will be tough.
3   Flour your hands. One at a time, pull pieces of dough from the lump and — with your hands — roll it into a rope, about the thickness of your thumb. With a sharp knife, cut the rope into 1-inch/2.5-cm pieces. They will look like plump little pillows. Dent each pillow lightly with your finger. Drop the

pieces, in one layer, on to the floured platter. Repeat (reflouring your hands as necessary) until all the dough is used.

4   Choose a shallow casserole and pour in a layer of the sauce. Have a slotted or mesh skimmer ready. When the water is boiling, drop in the gnocchi a few at a time. When they rise to the surface, skim them out, shake the skimmer over the pot to drain the gnocchi, and spread them out over the sauce. Repeat until all the gnocchi are cooked. Pour on the remaining sauce and toss *very gently*. Serve at once.

Note: To freeze Gnocchi, after forming them spread them out on a non-stick baking dish and freeze flat. When frozen gather into plastic bags and store in the freezer until needed. To cook from frozen, drop them — still frozen — a few at a time, into lightly salted, boiling water. When they rise to the top, skim them out.

Substitute one large sachet (4½ oz/120 g) of unseasoned potato flakes (Mr Mash or Waitrose brand) for the potatoes. Reconstitute them with water according to the directions on the box, but *do not* add milk or butter.

Polenta

Polenta, a staple of Northern Italy, is a sort of maize porridge, made from corn (maize) meal. Maize (along with tomatoes, potatoes, chocolate and many other now beloved foodstuffs) was unknown in Europe before the exploration of the New World; it's hard to believe that polenta — now so thoroughly identified with Alpine Italy (and the Swiss Ticino, right over the border) didn't exist in the region until the fifteen hundreds. Polenta is traditionally made by cooking the maize meal in water (or stock) in big copper pots, stirring all the while with a long, stout wooden stick. After almost an hour of constant stirring it is (if cooked firm) turned out on to a board to form a beautiful golden moon. The moon is then cut into portions (old-fashioned Italian cooks use a length of string). If it is cooked soft, it is spooned out into a fluffy, steaming, golden, well-seasoned heap. Polenta rivals mashed potatoes in deliciously comforting carbohydrate power; in fact it is one of the starchy wonders of the world.

It is possible to buy quick-cooking polenta, I am delighted to say: instead of taking almost an hour of strenuous stirring and cooking, it takes only 5-7 minutes of not-so-strenuous stirring and cooking. Serve it freshly cooked with stews, meat sauces, tomato sauces (with or without meatballs or sausages), or saucy vegetable dishes. It's particularly good with thick mushroom sauces that have been enhanced with reconstituted dried porcini. I'll never forget a visit to Lugano in the Ticino. I was a speaker at a week-long conference and was closeted for a week — along with all the other delegates — in a stiflingly posh hotel high on a hill above the town. We were fed 3 elaborate, over-designed meals a day. In the real world (the town below), it was polenta season, and it was porcini season, but the only polenta we saw was at one lunch-time: *tiny* diamond-shaped morsels of the stuff garnishing thick steaks of venison. At the end of the week the conference ended and I was finally released. Down the hill I sped to find that Lugano was in the midst of a wine and food festival. People were dancing in the streets . . . even more important, they were *cooking* in the streets. Strong men, with their sleeves rolled up over their bulging biceps, were stirring huge copper cauldrons filled with polenta. Long wooden tables and benches were set up everywhere. I settled down with a plateful (I mean a *large* plateful) of the steaming polenta smothered with a generous ladleful of porcini-mushroom ragoût. *Paradise*, that's what it was!

 ## BASIC POLENTA

Makes approximately 2½ pts/1.4 l cooked polenta

Polenta is fast and easy if you begin with quick cooking polenta (available in Italian delis, or see Mail Order Guide, page 153). I advise stirring the polenta into the hot stock just *before* the liquid comes to the boil, because once stirred together, the thick mixture is prone to violent, volcanic bubbling that can splatter all over the place. It's a good idea to wear a sturdy oven glove to protect your hand and arm during the few minutes of stirring. Buttermilk or a few tablespoons of fromage frais can be stirred into the just-cooked polenta to make it creamy, along with grated Parmesan cheese for a rich cheese flavour. The buttermilk or fromage frais, of course, is not at all traditional, but it is a delicious and healthy stand-in for the usual butter.

Leftover polenta is wonderful: you should always cook enough to have some later in the week. See box overleaf for instructions.

1¼ pts/700 ml very well-seasoned stock	6 oz/175 g quick-cooking polenta

1   In a large heavy pot, heat the stock until very hot, but not quite boiling. With a whisk, stir in the polenta.
2   Switch to a wooden spoon, then stir over a low heat for approximately 5 minutes until very thick and smooth. (Watch out for volcanic bubbles. Wear an oven glove to protect your hand and arm.) At this point, the polenta should be thick and cooked, and it should pull away from the sides of the pot in a mass as it is stirred. Be careful not to scorch it. Serve at once, or cool for later eating.

To Store Cooked Polenta

To store polenta for the next day, or later in the week, spread freshly cooked polenta on to a baking sheet, spoon it into a loaf pan or baking dish, or spoon into empty, clean tins (tomato tins, for instance). Cool, cover and refrigerate. When you are ready for it, it will unmould perfectly from its dish or tin.

To Heat Cooked, Chilled Polenta
1   Cut a square of the polenta. Put it in a small baking dish and cover with foil for the conventional oven, or microwave cling film for the microwave.
2   Heat in the conventional oven at 350°F, 180°C, Gas Mark 4 for 30-40 minutes, or in the microwave on Full for 6 minutes. If you have used the microwave, pierce the cling film with a sharp knife to release the steam, then carefully uncover.

To Grill Cooked, Chilled Polenta
1   Preheat the grill to its highest setting. Cover the grill tray with foil, shiny side up. Cut squares of polenta and place on the tray.
2   Grill, close to the heat, for approximately 2 minutes until speckled with brown. Turn and grill for a minute or two on the second side.

 POLENTA PIZZA

Serves 6-8

Polenta makes a tender base for a quickly made, festive and family-style pizza. If your family is small, divide the recipe into 2 pans — cook one and freeze the other for another day. The pizza is festive because of the colours — the vivid red of the sauce against the glowing yellow of the polenta — and because it's a particularly successful combination of taste and texture. How nice that such splendid food is also healthy!

1¼ pts/700 ml very well-	*courgettes, grilled aubergine,*
seasoned stock	*grilled peppers, crumbled*
6 oz/175 g quick-cooking	*sausage balls or meatballs*
Polenta	*6 oz/175 g Italian-style medium-*
1 pt/570 ml Tomato Sauce (page	*fat mozzarella cheese,*
107)	*drained, blotted dry and*
Toppings of your choice: braised	*shredded*
mushrooms, grilled	

---

1 Preheat the oven to 350°F, 180°C, Gas Mark 4.
2 Bring the stock to just below the boil in a large, heavy bottomed pot. Pour in the polenta, and cook, stirring constantly, for approximately 5 minutes. (Watch out for volcanic bubbles. Wear an oven glove to protect your hand and arm.) At this point, the polenta should be thick, cooked, and should pull away from the sides of the pot in a mass as it is stirred. Be careful not to scorch it.
3 Immediately pour and scrape the polenta on to a 15 × 10 inch/38 × 25 cm *non-stick* baking sheet. Smooth it with a spatula and build up the sides a bit. Put it in the oven to bake for 15 minutes.
4 Spread the baked polenta base with tomato sauce. Arrange topping ingredients over sauce. Sprinkle evenly with cheese. Bake for 10-15 minutes until cheese is melted.

♡Omit mozzarella cheese or use rendered mozzarella cheese (page 8).

Omit sausages and meatballs.

❋   POLENTA WITH MEAT SAUCE

This substantial and soul-warming meal is made from cooked polenta that has cooled and been chilled in clean tomato tins. Use what you want for a single meal, and refrigerate the rest for a later meal. (You could halve or quarter the recipe, but − as long as you are making polenta − why not make enough for several meals?) The chilled cylinder of polenta is sliced, topped with meat sauce and grated cheese, covered with another polenta slice, and baked until the whole thing is piping hot, and the cheese has melted. Can you imagine anything better on a cold blustery night?

2½ pts/1.4 l stock	Bolognese Sauce (page 114) or
Salt and freshly ground pepper	Stracotto (page 34), or
to taste	Sausage Sauce (page 113)
9 oz/250 g polenta	Mozzarella cheese

1. Season 2½ pt/1.4 l stock with salt and pepper. Bring it to just under the boil. Sprinkle in the polenta, stirring all the while. Simmer for 10 minutes. (Watch out for volcanic bubbles. Wear an oven glove to protect your hand and arm.)
2. Spoon the cooked polenta into 2 (14 oz/400 g size) clean empty tomato tins and leave to cool for ½ hour (or refrigerate until you need it).
3. Unmould the polenta (shake it out of the tins). Cut a slice of polenta, cover with 3-4 tablespoons of the meat sauce of your choice and top with an ounce or two of mozzarella cheese. Heat in the microwave for 2 minutes on full power, or in a 350°F, 180°C, Gas Mark 4 oven for 20-30 minutes.

 BROCCOLI POLENTA

Fills 3 (14-oz/400-g) tins

First cook the broccoli in the microwave, then add it to the polenta-cooking liquid, and stir in the polenta. By the time the polenta is done, the broccoli has broken up into bits and should be thoroughly amalgamated into the cooked polenta. The polenta can then be moulded into tins, sliced and layered with whatever sauce you like.

1 lb/450 g broccoli, cut into	9 oz/250 g polenta
florets	Salt and freshly ground pepper
2½ pts/1.4 l stock	to taste

1. Cook broccoli in the microwave on full power for 6-8 minutes, or steam over boiling water until tender.
2. Season the stock with salt and pepper. Bring to just below the boil and add the broccoli. Sprinkle in the polenta and bring back to the boil. Simmer for approximately 10 minutes. (Watch out for volcanic bubbles — wear an oven glove to protect your hand and arm.)
3. Spoon the polenta into 3 (14 oz/400 g size) clean, empty tomato tins and leave to cool for ½ hour (or refrigerate until

needed). Unmould (shake it out of the tins) and slice the polenta when you are ready to serve it.

Suggestions for serving:
1   Place 1 slice of polenta in a ramekin. Cover with Smoked Chicken Sauce (page 82). Cover with another slice of polenta. Top with Tomato Sauce (page 107) or tomato passato and sprinkle with Parmesan cheese. Cook in the microwave on high for 2 minutes, or bake in a 350°F, 180°C, Gas Mark 4 oven for 20-30 minutes. Flash under the grill if desired.
2   Serve slices of Broccoli Polenta as a base for any of the pasta sauces or stews, or serve with Italian Sausage Balls and Tomato Sauce.
3   Use Broccoli Polenta in the recipe for Bolognese Polenta, (page 103).

SAVOURY POLENTA CAKE WITH GARLIC AND SPRING ONIONS

Makes one 8-inch/20.5-cm cake

Serve this savoury polenta cake as you would serve a potato pudding (the texture is not dissimilar): as a starchy accompaniment to meat or poultry, or to non-starchy vegetarian dishes. As the cake bakes, the baking polenta along with the melting cheese, the spring onions and garlic perfume the air with an almost unbearably come-hither aroma. Members of your household will be queuing up at the dining table long before the cake is ready to emerge from the oven.

12 spring onions, trimmed and sliced thin	12 oz/350 g quick-cooking polenta
1-2 cloves garlic, minced	Salt and freshly ground pepper to taste
1½ pts/900 ml well-seasoned stock	6 tablespoons grated Parmesan cheese

1   Preheat the oven to 350°F, 180°C, Gas Mark 4.
2   Combine the spring onions, garlic and ½ pt/300 ml stock in a heavy-bottomed saucepan. Cover and boil for 5 minutes. Uncover and simmer briskly until the onions and garlic are tender, and the liquid is about gone.

3   Pour in the remaining stock, season with salt and pepper and bring almost to the boil. When just below boiling, pour in the polenta in a steady stream, stirring constantly with a whisk. Switch from the whisk to a wooden spoon, and stir and cook until the mixture is thick and smooth (about 5 minutes). (Watch out for volcanic bubbles; wear an oven glove to protect your hand and arm.) Stir in the Parmesan cheese.
4   Spoon and scrape the mixture into a non-stick, round (8-inch/20.5-cm diameter) cake tin with a removable bottom. Smooth the top with the back of a spoon. Bake for 25-30 minutes. Cool on a rack for 5 minutes. Slip out the bottom of the tin. Cut the pie into wedges to serve.

Sauces

'Italians say that only children, the infirm, and the
ill-mannered use soup-spoons as props for their forks
when picking up pasta. I think spoons serve a more
important function, that of getting up the sauce left at
the bottom of the bowl.'

James Beard, *Beard on Pasta*

 TOMATO SAUCE

Makes 1½ pts/900 ml

This is a basic tomato sauce, infinitely useful in so many ways.
Make it in quantity (2 or 3 times the recipe) and store it − in small
containers − in the freezer. With this sauce in the freezer, and a
selection of pasta in the store cupboard, a simple, deeply comforting meal can be on the table in minutes.

3 shallots, skinned and finely chopped	*1 tablespoon chopped fresh thyme (or ¼ teaspoon dried)*
2 cloves garlic, crushed	*1 tablespoon chopped fresh oregano (or ¼ teaspoon dried)*
Pinch cayenne pepper	
6 fl oz/175 ml stock	

107

6 fl oz/175 ml dry red wine,
    white wine or vermouth
1 tablespoon chopped fresh
    parsley
1 tablespoon chopped fresh basil
    (or ¼ teaspoon dried)

3 tins (14-oz/400-g each)
    chopped tomatoes
Salt and freshly ground pepper
    to taste
2 tablespoons tomato purée

---

1   Combine the shallots, garlic, cayenne pepper, stock, wine and
    herbs (if you are using dried herbs) in a heavy frying pan.
    Cover, bring to the boil, reduce the heat and simmer briskly
    for 5-7 minutes. Uncover and simmer until almost all the
    liquid has evaporated and the shallots are tender.
2   Stir in the tomatoes and season to taste. Simmer, partially
    covered, for 15 minutes. Stir in the tomato purée and the fresh
    herbs if you are using them and simmer for 5 minutes more.
    Taste and adjust seasonings. For a smooth sauce, purée the
    tomato mixture in a blender. If you like your tomato sauce
    chunky, leave it as it is.

♡ 🧸❄ 🥕 TOMATO-APRICOT SAUCE

Makes approximately 1½ pts/900 ml

I've never come across tomato-apricot sauce in Italy, and I've
never seen it mentioned in any of my reference books. In fact,
until I developed this recipe, I don't think there has been such a
thing. But one day I stopped and looked at the bowl of apricots
and tomatoes resting on my kitchen counter. They were sharing a
bowl for a few days while they slowly ripened at room temperature. The two fruits looked so beautiful and so natural together, I
suddenly *knew* they would make a superb sauce. And — combined with caramelized onion, garlic, sun-dried tomatoes, and
vermouth — so they did.

---

2 large Spanish onions, coarsely
    diced
3 large cloves garlic, crushed
10 fl oz/300 ml stock
2-3 tablespoons dry white
    vermouth
10 medium-sized ripe tomatoes,
    cut into chunks

4-5 firm ripe apricots, cut into
    chunks
6-7 sun-dried tomatoes, snipped
    (use scissors) — optional
Salt and freshly ground pepper
    to taste

---

1   Combine the onions, garlic and 6 fl oz/175 ml stock in a large,

heavy bottomed, non-reactive frying pan. Cover and bring to the boil. Boil for 5-7 minutes.

2   Uncover and cook briskly until the liquid is almost gone and the onions are beginning to stick. Pour in the vermouth and cook, stirring and scraping up the browned deposits in the pan.

3   When the onions are tender, browned and syrupy, stir in the ripe tomatoes, apricots and sun-dried tomatoes. Stir in the remaining stock and season to taste. Simmer, uncovered, for 20 minutes or until thick and the tomatoes and apricots have lost their shape. Cool.

4   Purée the sauce until smooth in the liquidizer, then rub through a non-reactive sieve. Refrigerate or freeze until needed.

> 'To be sure, every form of fanaticism can prove limiting.
> This also applies to food. Good cooking is an art form
> and as such it requires freedom and imagination, in
> order to be expressed fully. Everybody knows − should
> know − that some of the most celebrated dishes were
> created by mistake, or by a daring combination of
> ingredients that were, up to that moment, never used
> together.'
>
> Edda Servi Machlin, *The Classic Cuisine of the Italian Jews*

Variation:

♡ ❄ SPICY TOMATO-APRICOT SAUCE

Makes 3¼ pts/1.8 l

The Tomato-Apricot Sauce has a sweet and sour flavour, and a smooth texture; the Spicy Tomato Sauce has a piquant flavour and a chunky texture. Put together, they are quite extraordinary.

Combine the Tomato-Apricot Sauce with Spicy Tomato Sauce (page 112) and simmer together for a few minutes. (Try Veal-Mushroom Sausage Balls on a bed of this sauce, surrounded by Balsamic Braised Mushrooms.)

⏱ ❄ QUICK TOMATO SAUCE WITH CAPERS

Makes 1½ pts/900 g

A box of passata, a tin of tomatoes − an Italian infusion, a few herbs . . . What a lovely sauce for less than ½ hour's investment of time.

5-6 spring onions, trimmed and sliced	6-8 fl oz/175-225 ml stock
3-4 sun-dried tomatoes, snipped (use scissors) — optional	1 box (1 lb 2 oz/500 g) tomato passato
3-4 olives in brine, drained and sliced off their stones	1 tin (14 oz/400 g) chopped tomatoes
1 teaspoon drained capers	1 tablespoon fresh parsley
1-2 cloves garlic, minced	1 tablespoon fresh oregano
Pinch or two crushed dried chillies	Freshly ground pepper to taste

1   Combine the onions, sun-dried tomatoes, olives, capers, garlic, chilli and stock in a non-reactive frying pan. Cover and boil for 3-4 minutes. Uncover and simmer until the onions and garlic are tender and the liquid has cooked down considerably and become syrupy.
2   Stir in the passato and the chopped tomatoes. Simmer for approximately 15 minutes.
3   Add the fresh herbs and some freshly ground pepper. Taste and adjust seasonings if necessary.

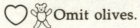 Omit olives.

 ARRABBIATA SAUCE

Makes 2 pts/1.1 l sauce

Pasta al Arrabbiata should make your hair stand on end, your tastebuds boogie and your digestive system go *Wowie Zowie*. In other words, it should have enough garlic and chilli peppers in it to curl your hair if it's straight, or to straighten it, if it's curly. I've eaten pretty potent versions of this in my time. A really zesty Pasta al Arrabbiata always puts me in mind of my friend Abe Lebewohl, proprietor of the 2nd Avenue Delicatessen on New York's Lower East Side, and his comment about a particularly garlicy Jewish speciality he once placed in front of my quivering nose: 'A delicate person doesn't eat this food.' So be warned. If you like subtlety, delicacy and understatement, turn the page. Do remember though, before you run away, the garlic is cooked into an infusion with stock and olive slivers, rather than fried in oil, so the sauce is not nearly as ferocious as it *could* be. Still, you'll *know* that you've eaten something with character (so will every-one else). If you are a dentist with a bunch of patients to treat tomorrow; if you are an actor with a love scene coming up; if your schedule lists an upcoming board meeting in a small enclosed room, then save this for another day. Otherwise, *enjoy!*

8 cloves garlic, peeled and roughly chopped	2 tins (12 oz/350 g each) chopped tomatoes
Several generous pinches of crushed dried chillies	4-5 large fresh ripe tomatoes, cored, skinned, seeded and roughly chopped
3-4 black olives, sliced off their stones	Salt and freshly ground pepper to taste
4-5 sun-dried tomatoes, snipped (use scissors) – optional	1-2 tablespoons tomato purée
Approximately 4 fl oz/110 ml stock	4-5 leaves shredded fresh basil
2-3 fl oz/50-75 ml dry white vermouth	

1 Combine the garlic, chillies, olives, sun-dried tomatoes, stock and vermouth in a heavy, non-reactive frying pan. Simmer, uncovered, until the garlic is very tender and the liquid about gone. Add more stock during the cooking if necessary.
2 Stir in the tinned tomatoes. Simmer for 5-7 minutes. Add the fresh tomatoes and season to taste. Simmer for 5-7 minutes more. Stir in the tomato purée and the basil. Let simmer for another 5 minutes.

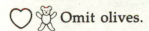 Omit olives.

 FAST PIZZA SAUCE

Makes 1 pt/570 ml

My son Shawm inspired this recipe. He has a way of opening a box of tomato passato, throwing in some herbs and plenty of pepper, and ending up with a marvellous pizza sauce. Before he learned to make yeast pizza dough from scratch, he used this sauce on bagel pizzas: split bagels topped with his quick sauce and shredded mozzarella, and grilled. This multi-ethnic recipe was the direct result of a summer spent half in Israel, half in Rome. (Yes, travel *is* broadening.)

10 thin spring onions, trimmed and sliced	Pinch or 2 crushed dried chillies
3 black olives in brine, drained and sliced off the stone	Pinch or 2 dried oregano
	6-8 fl oz/175-225 ml stock
3-4 sun-dried tomatoes, snipped (use scissors) – optional	1 box (1 lb 2 oz/500 g) tomato passato
1-2 cloves garlic, minced	Freshly ground pepper to taste

1 Combine the onions, olives, sun-dried tomatoes, garlic, chilli, oregano and stock in a non-reactive frying pan. Cover and boil for 3-4 minutes. Uncover and simmer until the mixture is almost dry and the onions and garlic are tender.

2 Stir in the tomato passato and grind in some pepper. Simmer for 10-15 minutes.

Omit olives.

SPICY TOMATO SAUCE

Makes 1¾ pts/1 l

Because I love fennel and chilli, this is my favourite sauce to use on pizza, and it's pretty good on pasta, too. The fennel seeds and chilli give it loads of pizzazz. (You wouldn't want a pizza that had no pizzazz, would you?)

4-5 cloves garlic, coarsely chopped	1 box (1 lb 2 oz/500 g) tomato passato
4-5 sun-dried tomatoes, snipped (use scissors) – optional	¼ teaspoon each fennel seeds and crushed dried chillies
½ pt/300 ml stock	1 heaped tablespoon tomato purée
2 tins (14 oz/400 g each) Italian tomatoes	Freshly ground pepper to taste

1 Combine the garlic, sun-dried tomatoes and stock in a heavy-bottomed frying pan. Cover and boil for 5 minutes. Uncover and simmer briskly until the liquid is almost gone, and the garlic is 'frying' in its own juices.

2 Stir in the tomatoes and their juices. With the open end of the tin, coarsely chop the tomatoes right in the pan. Stir in the passato. Add the fennel seeds and chillies. Simmer briskly for 20 minutes, until thick and savoury. Stir in the purée and ground pepper and simmer for 5 minutes more.

SAUSAGE SAUCE

Makes 2½ pts/1.4 l

This spicy meat sauce, based on my Slim Cuisine Italian Sausage Balls (page 28) is delicious tossed into sturdy pasta shapes (penne, pennoni, farfalle, ziti, etc.), layered with lasagne sheets, or rolled into cannelloni. As with many of the other sauces in this chapter, it pays to make a big batch, and store it in the freezer in small containers.

1 lb/450 g very lean minced pork	1 large onion, chopped fine
Finely chopped flesh of 3 baked aubergines (see page 44)	Salt and freshly ground pepper
1 teaspoon fennel seeds	2 tins (14 oz/400 g each) chopped tomatoes
¼ teaspoon crushed dried chillies	8 fl oz/225 ml tomato passato
3 cloves garlic, crushed	1 piece Parmesan rind
3 tablespoons dry red wine or dry white vermouth	2 tablespoons each shredded basil and chopped parsley

1   In a large bowl, combine the pork, chopped aubergine, fennel seeds, chillies, garlic, wine, onion, salt and pepper. Mix very well. If you have time, refrigerate the mixture for a few hours or overnight so that the flavour can develop.

2   Put the meat mixture into a large, heavy bottomed frying pan. Cook over a moderate heat, breaking up the lumps of meat as it cooks. When the onion is tender and the meat is cooked, drain in a colander over a bowl. Off the heat, line the frying pan with paper towels, return the meat to the pan, blot it with the overhang and slip out the towels.

3   Stir in the remaining ingredients, except for the shredded herbs. Simmer, stirring occasionally for 15 minutes or so, until the mixture is thick and savoury. Stir in the herbs, adjust the seasoning and simmer for 5 minutes more. Remove Parmesan rind before serving. Serve with Cannelloni (page 94), or toss with penne, pennoni, farfalle, ziti or use in lasagne.

BOLOGNESE SAUCE

⏱ ❄

Makes 2½ pts/1.4 l

Spaghetti bolognese has become quite a cliché in this country, but the real thing is a rarity. I have to admit that I am not about to right that wrong; this bolognese sauce is no more 'real' than some of the truly awful ones found in freezer cases and bad restaurants. But — need I say it? — this one is far from awful. The meat is augmented with roasted aubergine so that ½ lb/225 g of very lean minced beef yields 2½ pts/1.4 l of rich-tasting sauce. The vegetables impart a lovely, fresh sweetness to the sauce. I like bolognese sauce tossed with sturdy pasta shapes, as opposed to long, thin spaghetti; it's also very good with cannelloni, or layered with lasagne.

---

1 medium onion, chopped	2 tins (1 lb/450 g each) chopped
2 large cloves garlic, crushed	tomatoes
1 small carrot, peeled and diced	Chopped pulp of 1 (¾-1 lb/350-
fine	450 g) roasted aubergine
1 small red and 1 small yellow	(page 44)
pepper, peeled and chopped	4 heaped tablespoons tomato
8 fl oz/225 ml stock	purée
5-6 sun-dried tomatoes, snipped	Salt and freshly ground pepper
(use scissors) — optional	to taste
Pinch crushed dried chillies	1 tablespoon chopped fresh
½ lb/225 g very lean minced	oregano (¼ teaspoon dried)
beef, pork, or a combination	1 tablespoon chopped fresh basil
	(¼ teaspoon dried)

---

1   Simmer the onion, garlic, carrot and peppers in a non-stick, heavy-bottomed frying pan with the stock, sun-dried tomatoes and crushed chillies. Cook, covered, over a medium heat, until the onion softens. Uncover and simmer until the liquid has almost gone. Add the meat. Continue to stir and cook until the meat is completely cooked through and the onions are limp. Dump the mixture into a colander to drain away any fat. Off the heat, line the pan with paper towels, return the meat and blot with the overhang. Slide out the paper towels.

2   Add the chopped tomatoes, aubergine, tomato purée, salt, pepper and dried herbs if you are using them. Partially cover the frying pan and simmer for 20 minutes.

3   Season the sauce to taste, and add the fresh herbs, if using. Simmer, partially covered, for approximately 15 minutes

more, until the sauce is thick and the vegetables are tender. The sauce may be refrigerated for a day or so or frozen.

♡🐭❄🥕 INTENSE MUSHROOM PÂTÉ (SALSA AL FUNGHETTO)

Makes 1¼ pts/700 ml

Salsa al Funghetto is a Tuscan preparation; a very thick sauce (a pâté really) of mushrooms, similar to French Duxelles. The Tuscan method, of course, is to sauté the mushrooms in olive oil. The Slim Cuisine method of sautéing the mushrooms in stock yields an even more intense mushroom flavour than the original. I add a dash or 2 of soy sauce to bring out the mushroom flavour (you won't taste the soy sauce in the finished salsa), as well as soaked dried porcini mushrooms and their soaking water. The salsa is a basic staple to have on hand all the time. Make it in quantity and freeze it in small portions. Spread the intense paste on toasted country bread, toss it into pasta with tomato sauce, layer it in lasagne, roll it in cannelloni, spoon it on to polenta, *revel* in it; it is a mushroom experience to cherish.

1 oz/25 g dried porcini, rinsed under the cold water tap	3 fl oz/75 ml dry white vermouth
1 lb/450 g brown cap mushrooms, cleaned well	Several dashes soy sauce
4 fl oz/110 ml stock	Salt and freshly ground pepper to taste

1 Soak the dried mushrooms in warm water for 15 minutes. Remove from the water. Strain the water through two layers of paper towels, or a coffee filter. Reserve the soaking water.
2 Mince the mushrooms (including the soaked mushrooms) very, very finely. This is best done in a food processor if you have one. Quarter the brown cap mushrooms and put them into the food processor along with the soaked mushrooms, then pulse on and off until very finely minced. You will need to do this in two or more batches.
3 Empty the minced mushrooms into a deep, non-reactive frying pan. Add the stock, 2 fl oz/50 ml of the soaking water, vermouth and soy sauce, stirring well. The mushrooms will be barely moistened but it doesn't matter.
4 Cook over a moderate heat, stirring occasionally, until the mushrooms have rendered quite a bit of liquid. Turn the heat

up a little and simmer briskly, stirring occasionally, until the mushrooms are very dark, very thick and quite dry. Season to taste. Refrigerate or freeze until needed.

RICOTTA PESTO

Makes 12 fl oz/350 ml of sauce

Pesto, one of the most delicious sauces in the world, is a paste of basil, pine nuts, garlic and olive oil. For years now I've been making it with quark (creamy, non-fat curd cheese), instead of olive oil, and roasted garlic purée in place of raw garlic. The result is an exquisite lower fat basil sauce that couples the mellow taste and compelling texture of roasted garlic purée with the creaminess of quark. I thought I was being pretty innovative until I read Marcella Hazan's second book, *More Classic Italian Cooking*. She describes a Ricotta Pesto that she tasted in a restaurant on the Italian Riviera. The recipe, detailed in her book contains − in addition to 3 tablespoons of ricotta − ⅕ pint/110 ml of olive oil and 2 tablespoons of butter, and it contains raw garlic rather than roasted garlic, but, still, it shows that adding a creamy textured cheese to pesto sauce is not such an iconoclastic idea after all. If you use half-quark, half-ricotta, as detailed below, you will have lovely creaminess with minimal fat. The roasted garlic enhances the texture and contributes a gentle garlic taste, as opposed to a ferocious one.

10 tablespoons torn basil leaves	*¼ lb/110 g low-fat or medium-*
6 tablespoons roughly chopped	*fat ricotta cheese*
parsley	*¼ lb/110 g quark*
5 tablespoons freshly grated	*Purée from 1 head of roasted*
Parmesan cheese	*garlic (see page 43)*
1 oz/25 g pine nuts	*Salt and freshly ground pepper*
	to taste

1 Combine all the ingredients in the container of a food processor.
2 Process to a thick paste. Scrape into a bowl and refrigerate.

Variation: If you can't find ricotta cheese, make the pesto with ½ lb/225 g quark instead.

'Basil can be seen everywhere in Genoa. In the working-class districts, on the window-sills of tenement houses that are hundreds of years old and that have been reshaped, modernized, patched up but never pulled down and rebuilt, the herb flourishes in vases, saucepans and empty tins, tended with the same loving care that the inhabitants of the Alto Adige bestow on the geraniums with which they decorate their windows and balconies.'

Ada Boni, *Italian Regional Cooking*

Soups to soothe the soul: clockwise from the foreground: tomato-
fennel soup; bruschetta with tomatoes; simple minestrone; puréed
vegetable-bean soup.

Italian fish stew overflows with the bounty of the sea.

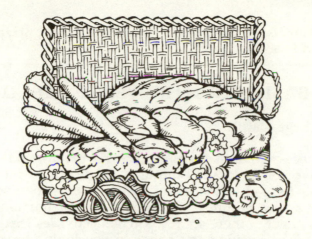

Bread

'Even the bread changes. In Puglia it is rich, crusty, and
yellow, full of flavor, whereas in Tuscany (Florence's
province) it has no salt and is desperately bland, as a
deliberate foil to the region's food, which is very salty.
When Dante was exiled from his beloved Tuscany he
described the bitterness of his homesickness by writing:
"How salty is the bread in other people's houses." '

Joanne Kates, *The Taste of Things*

Good Bread

Reproducing the bread of another country is almost impossible. Differences in flour, water, climate and fuel make it a very
difficult exercise indeed. In fact, in the same country, reproducing — in a particular region — the bread of another region
is hard enough. So, instead of trying to give you a 'real' Italian
bread, I'm giving you my favourite Peasant bread. It's crusty
with a sturdy (but not too heavy) crumb and a wonderfully
developed flavour. All you need is strong white bread flour
(right off the supermarket shelf), *fresh* yeast (buy it in some
health food stores, or — best of all — directly from your local
bakery), some sea salt, tap water, and . . . mashed potatoes. It's
the *potatoes* that give this bread its character, its deep flavour,
its marvellous texture and its keeping quality. Potatoes added
to home-baked breads that are baked with supermarket flour,
in ordinary home ovens, make all the difference in the world.

119

The potato dough also makes wonderful calzone, pizze, bread-sticks and sandwich rolls.

♡❄️🥕BASIC COUNTRY YEAST BREAD

Makes 1 large loaf

A food processor makes the early stages of bread-making a snap. It will save you at least 15 minutes of kneading. But after the dough has formed in the machine, it still must be kneaded by hand for a few minutes. Of course, this is not anything to complain about — there are few kitchen activities that are quite as much *fun* as getting one's hands in developing bread dough. See the box on page 122 for advice on preparing the dough if you have no food processor. This recipe will make one large loaf of bread. And see page 122 for lots of suggestions for other lovely things you can do with this dough.

½ oz/10 g fresh yeast	skins until tender and then
9-10 fl oz/275-300 ml warm water	pushed through a ricer or mouli
1 lb/450 g strong white flour	1 teaspoon sea salt
8 oz/225 g baking potatoes, baked and scooped out of their shells, or boiled in their	

1   Combine the yeast with 5 fl oz/150 ml water. Stir with a fork or tiny whisk to dissolve the yeast.
2   Combine the flour, potatoes and salt in the container of a food processor. Stir the remaining water into the yeast mixture. Turn on the processor and pour the yeast mixture gradually through the feed tube. Stop to scrape the mixture down occasionally. When the mixture forms a cohesive dough, stop the machine, gather up the dough and place it on a very lightly floured work surface.
3   Knead rhythmically until the dough is smooth and lively. This will take 5-10 minutes. Add a sprinkling of additional flour, only if the dough is hard to handle, but remember that this dough should be a little sticky. Too much flour will make the finished loaf too heavy. On the other hand, if the dough is too dry, add more water. You know the dough has been kneaded sufficiently when you can poke it with a finger and the indentation springs back. Form the dough into a smooth

ball and place it in a very lightly floured bowl. Dust the top sparingly with flour. Cover loosely with cling film. Put a roasting pan on the floor of the oven and fill it with boiling water. Put the bowl of dough in the oven and leave it to rise for 1-1½ hours, until doubled in bulk.

4   Punch the dough down and knead it a few turns to expel the gas. Let it rest, while you lightly flour a non-stick baking sheet. Remove the pan of water from the oven, and preheat the oven to 400°F, 200°C, Gas Mark 6.

5   Form the dough (by this time it is so lively it is practically talking back to you) into a plump round loaf. Put it on the floured baking sheet, cover loosely with cling film and leave in a warm quiet corner to double in bulk, ½-¾ of an hour. In the meantime, put the kettle on.

6   Put another baking dish of boiling water on the oven floor. Bake the bread for 40-55 minutes. Fill a clean spray bottle, or water pistol, with water and spray the bread several times during the baking. For the last few minutes of baking, turn the loaf upside down directly on the oven shelf. The bread is done when it is golden brown, and a knuckle-thump on the bottom produces a hollow sound. Although it is very difficult to wait, the flavour of this bread (and its variations) is best when it has cooled. In fact, it really is best, as far as flavour is concerned, on the second day.

♡❄︎🥕 COUNTRY BREAD USING INSTANT POTATO FLAKES

If you can find instant non-seasoned potato *flakes* (not those awful little pellets, and not powders), use them in the dough in place of fresh potatoes. You'll save some time, and the bread will still be splendid.

½ oz/10 g fresh yeast	flakes (Mr Mash or Waitrose
14 fl oz/375 ml warm water	brand)
1 large sachet (4½ oz/120 g)	1 lb/450 g strong white flour
instant, unseasoned potato	1 teaspoon sea salt

1   Combine the yeast with 5 fl oz/150 ml water. Stir with a fork or tiny whisk to dissolve the yeast.

2   Combine the potato flakes, flour and salt in the container of a food processor. Stir the remaining (9 fl oz/250 ml) water into the yeast mixture. Turn on the processor and pour the yeast

mixture gradually through the feed tube. Stop to scrape the mixture down occasionally. When the mixture forms a cohesive dough, stop the machine, gather up the dough and place it on a very lightly floured work surface. Continue as in master recipe — page 120.

If you want to make this recipe but you do not have a food processor, the dough can easily be mixed in a big bowl. It takes a little longer, but it's more fun — mixing and kneading is just about the most *immediate* and most therapeutic kitchen exercise there is.

1 Combine the flour, salt (and the dry potato flakes if you are using them) in a large warm bowl, mix with your fingers. If you are using fresh cooked riced potatoes, rub the potato into the flour until well amalgamated.

2 Make a well in the centre of the flour-potato mixture. Combine the yeast and water as described in the above recipe. Pour the liquid into the well. With your hand (or with a wooden spoon if you don't want to get your hands that messy) start mixing the flour into the liquid. Mix and work the mixture until it forms a rough but cohesive dough, then turn out on to a lightly floured surface and knead vigorously until the dough is smooth, satiny and lively. If the dough is too sticky and wet, add a bit more flour; if too dry, add a bit more water. You know the dough is ready when — if you poke it gently with your finger — the indentation springs back.

Bread Variations:
 WILD MUSHROOM BREAD

This makes a gorgeous bread with a subtle flavour of porcini, and a beautiful colour.

Soak 2 oz/50 g of dried porcini mushrooms in 1 pt/570 ml of very warm water for 20-30 minutes. Drain the mushrooms (save the water), rinse them under cold running water and chop them fine. Strain the soaking water through a coffee filter or several thicknesses of paper towels. Add the minced mushrooms to the flour-potato mixture. Replace the water with an equal amount of mushroom-soaking water. Proceed as in the basic recipe.

GARLIC BREAD

You want garlic bread? I'm going to give you garlic bread like you've never had in your life! Roast a large firm whole head of garlic and squeeze out the purée and push it through a non-reactive sieve, according to the directions on page 43. After the dough has had its first rising, punch it down with a rolling pin, roll it out into a flat oval. Spread the oval with the garlic purée. Fold the dough over the purée. Knead it vigorously until the puree is thoroughly amalgamated into the dough, then continue with the basic recipe.

WHOLEMEAL BREAD

Up to half of the strong white flour can be replaced with wholemeal bread flour.

FOCACCIA

Focaccia is flat bread, like a pizza with no filling. To make focaccia pull off lumps of Country Yeast dough (after the first rising), knead briefly, pat each into a round and − with a rolling pin on a lightly floured surface − roll each into an oval (⅛-¼-inch/0.25-0.5-cm thick). Put the ovals on to a lightly floured baking sheet, dent them in several places with your knuckles and bake at 400°F, 200°C, Gas Mark 6 until done (they will be well browned, and sound hollow when knocked on the bottom). Turn over for the last few minutes of cooking. Cool on a rack.

BALLOONED SANDWICH ROLLS

Once I was making focaccia in a big hurry, and − in my haste − forgot to knuckle-dent the ovals of dough. The purpose of the dents is to keep the flattish ovals of dough from ballooning up as they rise in the oven, so, of course, each oval did exactly that: balloon like mad. They were *fantastic*: hollow inside, and − when split − perfect for filling. So follow the recipe for focaccia, but do not knuckle-dent the ovals. Split the rolls while still warm, and fill with Pepper and Eggs, Sausages and Peppers, Smoked Turkey and Olive-Tomato Salad . . . you get the idea. These sandwich rolls are particularly good with the garlic bread dough (see above).

BREAD STICKS

Pull off a lump of dough (after its first rising), knead briefly, and roll into an ⅛-inch/0.25-cm thick rough rectangle. With a sharp knife, cut the rectangle into strips approximately ½-inch/1-cm thick. Lay them on a lightly floured baking sheet and bake for 7-12 minutes at 400°F, 200°C, Gas Mark 6 until crisp and brown. Turn over for the last few minutes. Cool on a rack.

If Time is a Problem

The long ritual of kneading and risings can be manipulated to suit you, so that you don't have to spend long swatches of time at home tied to your bread dough. Prepare the dough (but use only ¼ oz/5 g of fresh yeast, instead of ½ oz/10 g) through step 3, but once it's in its warm bowl don't leave it to rise for its full time. Let it sit in a warm, draught-free place for 10-15 minutes only; just long enough to get started. Then drape the dough loosely with a clean tea towel, and put the whole bowl in the refrigerator where it can rise *slowly* overnight (or even longer). On the next day, punch down the dough. It can go back in the fridge for a 2nd slow rising, if you are not ready to bake, or − if you want to bake a pizza, or a small loaf, pull off as much as you want to use, and return the rest to the fridge. It can remain for up to 3 days, simply punch it down each day.

 # BRUSCHETTA WITH MELTED MOZZARELLA

Bruschetta is a slice of lightly toasted bread rubbed with garlic and then topped with tomatoes or tomatoes and cheese (or with Mushroom Pâté [page 115] or grilled peppers or fried peppers), or whatever strikes your fancy. Serve as a snack, first course, or an informal light meal.

Thick slices of Country Bread or baguettes	Ripe tomatoes, sliced
	Freshly ground pepper
Garlic cloves, split	Shredded fresh basil leaves
A few black olives packed in brine, drained and sliced off the stone	Italian-style medium-fat mozzarella cheese, drained, blotted dry and shredded
Tomato sauce (page 107)	

---

1   Preheat the grill. Line the grill tray with foil, shiny side up. Place the grill rack on the tray.
2   Toast the bread very lightly, on one side only, under the grill.

Rub the toasted side with the cut garlic and olive. Mince all the garlic and olives and set aside.

3   Spread the toasted side of the bread with a very thin layer of tomato sauce. Top with a layer of sliced tomatoes. Grind some pepper on the tomatoes and sprinkle with the minced garlic and olives. Sprinkle on the basil.

4   Scatter the mozzarella over the whole thing. Grill for a minute or two, or until the mozzarella melts.

♡ Omit olives, use rendered mozzarella cheese (page 8).

Variation

⏱♡🥕 BRUSCHETTA WITH TOMATOES

Follow the above recipe through step 3 only.

Pizza

How has such perfectly balanced, splendidly healthy, altogether glorious food as pizza become synonymous with fast food, junk food, the lowest of the low, gastronomically speaking? Frozen pizza, chill-cabinet pizza, High Street pizza chains, pizza home delivered by motor bike — pizza, pizza *everywhere*, but — alas — very little of it is what I'd call edible. In fact, with the exception of the excellent Pizza Express chain, very little of it is what I'd call *pizza*. As I write this, I have in front of me a box of frozen pizza. Each slice, according to the information on the box, simply overflows with 'apple chunks, mozzarella cheese, animal and vegetable fat, salt, sugar, modified starch . . .' It is, in fact, apple-custard pizza. My staff and I sat down to sample a piece of this oddity: rampant curiosity forced us to do it. Rampant disgust then forced us to spit it out into paper towels and then run madly around the kitchen desperately seeking glasses of water, bites of bread, hard candies, *anything* to obliterate the foul taste of this so-called 'pizza'. What is the world coming to? Of course, most fast-food pizze do not quite reach this level of depravity, but they are certainly not representative of anything approaching the simple goodness of true pizza. A *real* pizza is a lovely thing.

How can I ever forget my first pizza? It was 1955, I was barely 15 years old and my gastronomic sensibilities were yet undeveloped. My mother was a dreadful cook; she didn't understand food (and she certainly didn't *like* it particularly). I *knew* that there were exciting and fulfilling gastronomic adventures to be had out in the world, but — except for the

---

occasional exhilarating meal in the Jewish delis of New York —
I hadn't really connected with them yet. One evening, a most
interesting and worldly young person (he was 16 — a man of
the world) took me out to eat. These were the days before fast
food, before franchised conglomerate-produced pizza, before
frozen and chill-cabinet pizza. In the America of those days, if
you were lucky enough to live in a city with a sizeable Italian
community, you could eat pizza in a Pizzeria run by real
Italians (from Naples), who had a mania for perfection, and a
burning need to recreate the pizza (and the ambience) of their
homeland. This young man took me to just such a place. The
pizza was baked in a wood-burning oven. It was a huge wheel
of perfect, crusty, wheaty, burnished dough spread with a real
tomato sauce (freshly made by the proprietor) and topped with
brown-speckled, pully, oozy, molten mozzarella cheese. Flecks
of oregano and chunks of fennel-studded sausage garnished
the bubbling pie. With a flourish, the proprietor wielded a
pizza cutter and divided the huge pie into wedges. The first
bite burned the roof of my mouth, the second was a glory of
rich sauce, spicy pepper, crusty bread, the third — and all the
rest — sheer heaven. I had *never* eaten such a thing in my life.
What does one do with the person who brings this kind of
gastronomic revelation into one's life? Reader, I married him.
There were seven years from that first pizza to marriage, and
those years — (and the thirty since then) were filled with all
sorts of extraordinary experiences, gastronomic and otherwise.
But I don't think any of them, however extraordinary, had
quite the impact of that first pizza.

I look at that apple-custard abomination, and many other
so-called pizzas of today and I wonder: how did such a perfect
food become so debased? Pizza is easy to make at home: good
bread dough, carefully made tomato sauce, a scattering of
mozzarella cheese . . . Why not try it yourself? Until you
actually do it, you can't imagine the excitement of producing a
real pizza in your own kitchen.

 # PIZZA

Makes 4 small pizze, or 2 large ones

| *Basic Country Bread dough* | *Toppings (see below)* |
| (*page 120*) | |

1   Prepare the dough and give it its first rise. Punch it down and divide it into quarters (or halves, if you want larger pizza). Knead each piece briefly, form it into a compact round and leave it on a lightly floured board, under a cloth, to rest for a few minutes.
2   Preheat the oven to 400°F, 200°C, Gas Mark 6. On a lightly floured surface, roll a section of dough out into a circle, rolling from the centre out to the edges, turning the dough as you fold. It doesn't need to be a perfect circle, so there's no need to fuss with it too much. Put the circle on to a lightly floured baking sheet. Spread the sauce on to the dough, leaving a 1-inch/2.5-cm border all around. Sprinkle on any additional ingredients.
3   When the oven is thoroughly hot, put the pizza in and bake for 15-25 minutes, until the filling is bubbly, and the edges of the dough are puffed and golden. Slide the pizza on to a serving plate or a board and cut into wedges.

Toppings for Pizza
Tomato sauce and mozzarella cheese are classic, but so is tomato sauce with no cheese, or − for that matter − cheese with no tomato sauce. Add whatever you like: strips of well-trimmed Parma ham; grilled courgettes, peppers and/or aubergine; crumbled meatballs or Slim Cuisine Italian sausages; cooked fresh spinach; raw, ripe tomato slices or cubes; braised fennel; courgettes with sun-dried tomatoes; feel free to design the pizza of your dreams.

♡ Use rendered mozzarella (page 8), tomato sauce and vegetables as toppings.

Use any of the toppings except the meaty ones.

> 'I did it. In one year I lost 130 pounds. It was at that point, when I weighed 190 pounds, that I went into the pizza business. I figured that if I couldn't eat it, I could become a pizza voyeur and sell and smell it.'
>
> Larry Goldberg, *Goldberg's Diet Catalog*

FILLED PIZZA WITH SPINACH, RICOTTA AND PARMA HAM

A pizza with a top *and* bottom crust, with the filling hidden between them, is beautiful to behold (and delightful to eat). Fill it with the Spinach-Ricotta mixture given below, fill it with grilled peppers (red and yellow), or fill it with any of the filling suggestions on pages 127 and 129.

½ batch bread dough prepared through step 4 (page 120)	*A few slices slivered, well-trimmed Parma ham*
Spinach-Ricotta filling (see below)	*Approximately 4 oz/110 g shredded mozzarella cheese*
	Freshly ground pepper to taste

1   Preheat the oven to 400°F, 200°C, Gas Mark 6.
2   On a lightly floured surface, roll half the dough out into a circle, rolling from the centre out to the edges, turning the dough as you fold. It doesn't need to be a perfect circle, so there's no need to fuss with it too much. Put the circle on to a lightly floured baking sheet. Spread the spinach-ricotta mixture over the dough. Sprinkle over the ham and mozzarella cheese. Grind on some pepper.
3   Roll out the other half of the dough, lay over the top of the pizza and pinch the edges together to seal. Bake in the oven for 20-25 minutes, until a knuckle thump produces a hollow sound.

 Omit parma ham.

 # SPINACH-RICOTTA FILLING

Makes approximately ½ pt/300 ml

1 lb/450 g raw spinach, well washed and trimmed of any tough stems	*1 lb/450 g low- or medium-fat ricotta cheese*
	Salt and freshly ground pepper to taste

1   Put the spinach into a large, non-reactive pot. There is no need to add liquid; the water that clings to the leaves from its washing will be sufficient. Cook over a high heat, stirring constantly, until the spinach is just tender. It should remain bright green. (This takes scant minutes.) Drain well and cool.
2   Combine the ricotta and spinach in the container of a food processor. Season to taste. Pulse on and off until the mixture forms a green-and-white flecked rough purée. Do not over-blend: it should not be a mush.

STUFFED LOAVES

Makes 2 loaves

I love the surprise of a freshly baked loaf with a hidden filling, baked right into the loaf.

Basic bread dough (see page 120)   *Filling of your choice (see list, below)*

---

1 Prepare the basic dough through to step 4 (page 120). Cut the dough into quarters. Form each quarter into a smooth ball.
2 With a rolling pin, on a lightly floured surface, roll one of the balls of dough out into a 7-8-inch/18-20.5-cm diameter circle. Put the circle on a lightly floured baking sheet. Arrange the filling on the circle. Roll another ball of dough into a circle slightly larger than the first. Lay it over the filling. Tuck the ends under the bottom circle all around the perimeter and pinch shut. Repeat with the remaining two balls of dough. Put the tray in a warm place and leave for about 20 minutes, until they have risen.
3 Bake at 425°F, 220°C, Gas Mark 7 for 25-35 minutes. They are done when a knuckle thump on the bottom produces a hollow sound.

Suggested Fillings for Calzone, Filled Breads and Stuffed Loaves
   Ricotta and a good dollop of tomato sauce (see sauce chapter)
   Mozzarella cheese (with or without tomato sauce) – if you wish add meatballs or sausages, to both the ricotta, and the mozzarella
   Stracotto
   Grilled peppers, or any grilled vegetable

   Courgettes with sun-dried tomatoes

   Salsa alla Funghetto (Intense Mushroom Pâté, page 115)

CALZONE AND FILLED ROLLS

A calzone is a folded pizza. Instead of spreading the filling on the dough, and then baking open-faced, the dough is folded over the filling – like an Italian version of a Cornish Pasty. A filled roll is simply a small, filled loaf.

1   Prepare the basic dough through to step 4 (page 120). Cut the dough into quarters or eighths, and form each piece into a smooth ball. With a rolling pin, on a lightly floured surface, roll each ball into a circle.

To make Calzone:-

2   Put some filling (see suggestions, page 129) across the centre of each circle. Fold over and pinch the ends to seal. Put the calzone on a lightly floured, non-stick baking tray.

To make filled rolls:-

2   Arrange the filling on the circle and roll into a cylinder. Pinch ends closed. Place on a lightly floured non-stick baking tray.

3   Leave, loosely covered, in a warm place for 20 minutes to rise. Bake at 400°F, 200°C, Gas Mark 6 for approximately 15 minutes (for small ones) or approximately 25 minutes (for the larger ones). They are done when they sound hollow when knuckle thumped on their bottoms.

 FIG BREAD

Serve this citrus-and-vanilla-scented fig-filled bread in wedges for breakfast, tea, picnics, or as a special treat in packed lunches. If the figs are left whole, the cross section of plump fig slices in each wedge looks very dramatic. Chopped, the figs make a more compact filling – both are delicious.

½ oz/10 g fresh yeast	*Slivered zest of 1 orange and 1*
14 fl oz/375 ml very warm water	*lemon*
1 tablespoon mild runny honey	*Pinch salt*
3 tablespoons skimmed milk	*1 teaspoon natural vanilla*
powder	*essence*
1 large sachet (4½ oz/120 g)	*1 batch glazed figs (page 139) –*
instant potato flakes	*the figs can be left whole, or*
Approximately 1 lb/450 g strong	*chopped. Either way the*
white flour	*stems should be removed*

1   Combine the yeast with 5 fl oz/150 ml warm water and the honey. Stir with a fork or tiny whisk to dissolve the yeast.

2   Combine the milk powder, potato flakes, flour, zests, salt and vanilla essence in the container of a food processor. Stir the

remaining water into the yeast mixture. Turn on the processor and pour the yeast mixture gradually through the feed tube. Stop to scrape the mixture down. Process until the mixture forms a dough. Remove to a floured board and knead, adding flour as necessary, until the mixture forms a smooth, not-too-sticky dough. It is kneaded sufficiently when a finger indentation springs back. Form the dough into a ball, lightly dust the dough with flour, and put it into the bowl, loosely covered with cling film. Leave it to rise until doubled in bulk (see page 120), approximately 1½ hours.

3   Punch the dough down and knead it a few times on a lightly floured surface to expel the gas. If it is very sticky, knead in a bit of flour, but avoid adding too much, or the dough will be heavy. Cut the dough into 2 equal pieces, form each piece into a smooth ball, and let rest while you preheat the oven to 400°F, 200°C, Gas Mark 6.

4   On a lightly floured surface, roll one piece of dough into a circle approximately 10 inches/25.5 cm in diameter. Put the dough on to a non-stick baking sheet that has been lightly dusted with flour or polenta (maize meal). Spread the figs and all their juices over the dough, leaving a 1-2-inch/2.5-5-cm border all around. Roll out the second piece of dough so that it is a little bigger than the first circle. Drape it over the fig-rolled base and tuck the edges under all around. Pinch closed.

5   Bake for 20-35 minutes (it is done when it is golden and a knuckle thump on the bottom produces a hollow sound). For the last 10 minutes or so of baking, turn it upside down, so that the loaf browns evenly. Cool on a rack.

⊕ ❄ ⸙ LUCY'S MOZZARELLA SCONES

Makes 13 scones

Lucy Kent (aged 12) developed these Slim Cuisine Scones. What a nice marriage of Italian and English culinary ideas they are.

---

8 oz/225 g self-raising flour	Approximately ¼ pt/150 ml
½ teaspoon salt	skimmed milk
7 oz/200 g mozzarella cheese,	½ tablespoon Parmesan cheese,
grated	grated

---

1   Preheat the oven to 425°F, 220°C, Gas Mark 7.

2   Sift the flour and salt into a bowl. Rub the mozzarella cheese into the flour. Add the milk a little at a time, until you have enough to form a soft, but not sticky, dough. Mix with a round-bladed knife.
3   Put the dough on to a lightly floured surface and knead very lightly. Roll it out and − using a 2½-inch/6-cm wide, 1¼-inch/3-cm deep cutter − cut into rounds.
4   Line a baking tray with greaseproof paper and put the scones on to the tray. Sprinkle a bit of Parmesan cheese over the top of each scone. Bake in the preheated oven for approximately 15 minutes until risen and golden brown. Serve hot or cooled.

Desserts

'Drama, drama, drama! The Italian meal itself is an opera
. . . The predictable summit of the opera, whatever may
have happened in between, comes at the closing climax,
with the entire cast crowding the stage shouting its
heads off while the kettledrums explode in the orchestra
pit. The object now is no longer to arouse the appetite,
but to sate it; and this is the function performed by the
rich Italian desserts, dramatized to the limit.'

Waverley Root, *The Best of Italian Cooking*

 ## CHERRY COMPÔTE

Makes 2 pts/1.1 l

Make this compôte with fresh cherries only. The compôte is
uncooked: the cherries macerate overnight in a combination of
citrus juices and zest, vanilla (use only *natural* vanilla essence)
and orange liqueur. The aromatic cherries are wonderful on their
own or − for a totally sybaritic experience − as a garnish to Deep
Chocolate Sorbet (page 149).

---

1 lb 12 oz/800 g cherries, halved
  and stoned
Juice of 1½ oranges

4 tablespoons orange liqueur
  (Cointreau or Grand
  Marnier)

Juice of 1 lemon	2 teaspoons natural vanilla
Slivered zest of ½ orange	essence
Slivered zest of ½ lemon	NutraSweet to taste

1   Combine all ingredients and let macerate overnight.

⊕ ¶PEACHES AND CREAM WITH MERINGUES

When ripe, silken, deeply flavoured peaches are in season, combine them with orange liqueur and natural vanilla essence, heap them lavishly into ready-made meringue nests, top with clouds of honeyed fromage frais, and drizzle with Spiced Red Vermouth Syrup. Don't even think of substituting tinned peaches. In season, this — simple though it is — is a showstopper.

6 large, ripe peaches	1 tablespoon mild runny honey
2-3 tablespoons orange liqueur	1 carton (1 lb 2 oz/500 g)
(Cointreau or Grand	fromage frais
Marnier)	Store-bought meringue nests
2 teaspoons natural vanilla	Spiced Red Vermouth Syrup
essence	(page 140)
Light brown sugar	

1   Halve the peaches and discard the stones. Cut them into
    ¾-1-inch/1.5-2.5-cm cubes. Work over a large bowl to catch
    the juices. Combine the peach cubes in the bowl with the
    liqueur, 1 teaspoon vanilla essence and a bit of sugar if the
    peaches are not sweet enough.
2   Stir the honey and the remaining vanilla essence into the
    fromage frais.
3   To serve, put a meringue nest on to a plate. Heap the peaches
    and their juices in, over and around each nest. Be lavish.
    Drizzle some Red Vermouth Syrup over the peaches. Top
    with a *very* generous dollop of the fromage frais. Sprinkle
    with a pinch of brown sugar.

⊕ ¶ PEACH-AMARETTI MESS

Like the Italian Root-Vegetable Gratin and Lucy Kent's Mozzarella Scones, this is an Italianization of an English classic. Eton
Mess is a delicious jumble of crumbled meringues, smushed
strawberries and whipped cream. I've often served a Slim

134

Cuisine version substituting fromage frais for the whipped cream. Peaches and Amaretti (almond-flavoured meringue) biscuits substituted for the strawberries and plain meringues give the classic an Italian accent. Cross cultural cookery: I love it!

Ripe, juicy, flavourful peaches	*Crushed Amaretti biscuits*
Fromage frais flavoured with a	
bit of honey, and the pulp of a	
vanilla pod	

1   Halve and stone the peaches, and dice them (no need to peel them). Set aside a few of the peach cubes; put the rest into a bowl and mash with a potato masher, until they are slightly pulped and their juices are flowing.
2   Stir together the mashed peaches, their juices and the fromage frais. Fold in the peach cubes and the crushed Amaretti biscuits. Serve in glass goblets.

 # STUFFED PEACHES

Makes 12 halves

Peaches that have been hollowed out, filled with peach pulp and crumbled Amaretti, and baked in Marsala until they are meltingly tender (but not at all mushy), can be served warm or at room temperature — either on a pool of the cooking juices, or on a pool of Spiced Red Vermouth Syrup. Make them extra special by piping a dollop of Orange-Ricotta Cream on to the centre of each one.

7 ripe, firm peaches	*6 fl oz/175 ml medium-sweet*
3 pairs Amaretti biscuits	*Marsala, or sherry*
¼ teaspoon natural vanilla	*Spiced Red Vermouth Syrup*
essence	*(page 140) (optional)*
3 fl oz-75 ml orange liqueur	*Orange-Ricotta Cream (page*
(Cointreau or Grand	*147) (optional)*
Marnier)	

1   Preheat the oven to 375°F, 190°C, Gas Mark 5.
2   Carefully halve the peaches. (Work over a bowl to catch any juices.) Remove the stones. Trim any bits of peach flesh off the stones and add them to the juices. Chop up 2 of the peach halves and put in the bowl with the juices. Using a teaspoon,

slightly hollow out the depressions in the remaining peach halves, so that they will hold the filling. Add the peach pulp that you have scooped out to the bowl. Place the peaches, skin side down in a baking dish that holds them snugly in one layer.

3 Crumble the Amaretti biscuits and stir them into the peach juices and chopped peach bits. Stir in the vanilla essence and ½ teaspoon of orange liqueur. Combine the remaining orange liqueur with the Marsala or sherry.

4 Fill each peach half with an equal amount of the Amaretti mixture. Pour 4-6 fl oz/110-175 ml of the Marsala mixture around the peaches. Sprinkle them with another 2-3 table-spoons of the mixture.

5 Bake, uncovered, for 10-12 minutes. Sprinkle them evenly with another 3-4 tablespoons of the Marsala mixture and bake for 8-10 minutes more. The peaches should not lose their shape.

6 With a slotted spoon, remove the peaches to a pretty serving dish. Serve the peaches warm or at room temperature, on a pool of the Vermouth Syrup if you are using it, or else on a pool of the boiled-down cooking juices. If you wish, pipe a dollop of Orange-Ricotta cream on to the centre of each peach half.

BAKED PEARS

Makes 8 halves

Ripe firm pears take beautifully to baking. Peel them first and then bake in Marsala and citrus juices. Serve them filled with Marsala and orange-scented Pear Ice Cream (recipe follows), or a dab of Orange-Ricotta Cream (page 147), although they taste just fine unadorned, as well.

4 fl oz/110 ml medium-sweet Marsala or sherry	*Juice and slivered zest of ½ lemon*
Juice and slivered zest of 1 large orange	*4 pears, ripe but firm*

1 Preheat the oven to 375°F, 190°C, Gas Mark 5.
2 Pour the liquids into a shallow, non-reactive baking dish and add the citrus zest.
3 Peel the pears and cut off the stem. Dip in the Marsala

mixture to prevent the pears darkening. Halve each pear and dip again. With a teaspoon, scoop out the cores. Rub the cavities with the Marsala mixture. Place the pears, cored side up, in the dish.

4   Bake uncovered for 20-30 minutes, until just tender. With a slotted spoon, transfer them to a plate. Drain all the juices into a small saucepan and boil until thickened and syrupy. Pour the juices over and around the pears (reserve a bit of the juices). Serve warm or at room temperature. Fill each pear half with either Pear Ice Cream (see below), or Orange-Ricotta Cream (substitute Marsala for the orange liqueur) (see page 147). Drizzle some of the reserved syrupy juices over the filling in each pear.

 # PEAR ICE CREAM

Makes 15 fl oz/400 ml

This is instant Slim Cuisine ice cream at its best. If you keep frozen pear cubes ready to go in your freezer, the ice cream is ready to eat in less than 5 minutes. Because the ice cream contains no air, no sugar, and no fat of any kind, it freezes harder than a brick, so make it and serve it.

8 oz/225 g frozen pear cubes, do not thaw (see note)	1 teaspoon natural vanilla essence
1 teaspoon Marsala	NutraSweet to taste
1 teaspoon orange liqueur	5-6 fl oz/150-175 ml buttermilk

1   Put the frozen pears into the container of a food processor. Add the Marsala, orange liqueur and vanilla essence. Sprinkle in a small amount (1-2 teaspoons) of NutraSweet. Pour in 3 fl oz/75 ml of the buttermilk. Turn on the machine and let it process for a minute or so.

2   Turn off the machine, scrape down the sides, then process again, pouring in a few more ounces of buttermilk. Process for another minute or two, stop and scrape down the sides again, and taste for sweetness. Add more NutraSweet if necessary, then process until the mixture forms a smooth, beautifully creamy ice cream. Serve at once, or store in the freezer for up to an hour.

Note: To freeze pears: choose ripe pears, cube them (no need to peel them first), spread out on non-stick cooking trays and freeze solid. When frozen, gather up the pieces into plastic bags and store in the freezer until needed. If they freeze together into a solid clump, knock on the counter a few times to separate them.

If you keep the frozen pears ready in the freezer, this is the quickest dessert imaginable.

CARAMELIZED PEARS WITH RICOTTA CREAM

Serves 2-4

Every night my husband — right after the main course — looks at me with those big baby blues, and asks, 'What's for pud?' Sometimes he just says, 'WFP?' His expectations are high — he doesn't want a mere pudding, he wants delirious ravishment of his taste-buds. I like to play a game with myself. I rarely plan the dessert course. When he turns those limpid blue beams on me and pops the inevitable question, I spring into action. Open the fridge, scrutinize the interior, grab a few likely ingredients, fling them around: what interesting new dish will emerge from tonight's game, and how fast can I set it on the table? It's the kind of cooking I love to do best of all — total improvisation with the inspiration of seasonal ingredients and a dessert-loving husband to egg me on. These baked pears were a result of one evening's inspiration; serve them warm in their caramelized juices, topped with the cold ricotta cream. It's a lovely pud (my husband *loved* it).

Pears

1 orange	1 vanilla pod
1 lemon	½-1 tablespoon caster sugar
4 firm, ripe pears	1 tablespoon orange liqueur
½ pt/300 ml red vermouth	(Cointreau or Grand
1 cinnamon stick	Marnier)

Topping

½ lb/225 g low- or medium-fat	½-1 tablespoon icing sugar
ricotta cheese or quark	½ tablespoon orange liqueur

1   Squeeze the juice of ½ orange and ½ lemon into a bowl. Peel

the pears, and dip them in the citrus juices to prevent darkening. Halve and core them, and dip again. Cut each half in half, and put them in a non-reactive frying pan with the citrus juice from the bowl, the slivered zest of ¼ orange and ¼ lemon, the vermouth, cinnamon stick, vanilla pod, sugar and the liqueur. Bring to the boil. Boil, uncovered, stirring frequently until the pear quarters are tender. With a skimmer or slotted spoon, remove the pears to the bowl, leaving the liquid behind.

2   Boil down the liquid until it is thick and syrupy. Pour and scrape this liquid into a small jug. Return the pears to the frying pan, along with the juice of the remaining ½ orange and ½ lemon.

3   Stir and cook quickly (and gently so that the pears do not break up) until the pears are richly glazed. Spoon the pears into small glass goblets. Pour some of the vermouth syrup over each.

4   Put the ricotta into the processor with the remaining ingredients (if using quark, you may need a touch more sugar) and process until perfectly smooth. With a rubber spatula, dollop the cheese into the goblets, and then spread it so it completely covers each serving of pears. Serve at once.

 # GLAZED FIGS

Makes 1 pt/570 ml

Dried figs, simmered in vermouth that has been spiked with orange liqueur, citrus juices and zests, and flavoured with cinnamon and vanilla, are delicious on their own or as a filling in Fig Bread (page 130). The glazed figs, well covered, will keep in the fridge for weeks.

1 lb/450 g ready-to-eat (pre-soaked) dried figs	*Juice and slivered zest of ½ orange*
8 fl oz/225 ml red vermouth	*Slivered zest of ½ lemon*
1 tablespoon orange liqueur (Grand Marnier or Cointreau)	*1 cinnamon stick*
	1 vanilla pod
	4 fl oz/110 ml water

1   Combine all the ingredients in a non-reactive saucepan.
2   Simmer briskly, stirring occasionally, until the liquid has reduced to a thick syrupy glaze and the figs are plumply tender.

SPICED RED VERMOUTH SYRUP

Makes approximately ½ pt/300 ml

Red Vermouth Syrup can be served hot or cold as a sauce for baked or raw fruit.

1 bottle red vermouth	1 cinnamon stick
Juice and slivered zest of 2 large oranges	1 vanilla pod
	8 fl oz/225 ml water
Juice and slivered zest of 2 large lemons	4-5 tablespoons sugar

1   Combine all the ingredients, except the sugar, in a wide, non-reactive pan, and bring to the boil. Boil until reduced to about half.
2   Stir in the sugar and boil for about 4-5 minutes more, until thickened and syrupy. Cool and store in the refrigerator. Remove the cinnamon stick and vanilla pod before using. (Scrape out the vanilla pulp and stir it into the syrup. Save the scraped pod for flavouring sugar or NutraSweet.) Serve with fruit salads, berries, Stuffed Peaches (page 135), or sliced oranges.

 # TIRAMISU

Fills a 12 × 7-inch/30.5 × 18-cm baking dish

Tiramisu seems to be everyone's favourite dessert. It is so ubiquitous, not only in Italy but in Italian restaurants all over the world, that it feels as if it is an old traditional recipe – several generations old at least. But Tiramisu is only 15-20 years old, and not characteristic of any particular region. It's simply made of sponge fingers and mascarpone cheese (sometimes the mascarpone is mixed with double cream and/or egg yolks). The whole thing is then topped with grated chocolate. Sponge fingers are not so bad, health-wise – they are made with whole eggs, so they do contain some fat, but no other fat is used – unless you have a cholesterol problem, or are on a weight-*loss* diet, they can be used occasionally in elegant desserts. But mascarpone? It's more than 80 per cent fat – actually higher in fat than double cream. Can you *imagine* eating such a thing, no less adding extra cream and egg yolks to it? You might as well butter your arteries and have done with it! But don't despair. In no way is the Slim Cuisine

Tiramisu a pale imitation of the killer original. It uses the same sponge fingers (or home-made fat-free ones, see note on page 143), but it substitutes medium- or low-fat ricotta (or ricotta mixed with quark to bring the fat down even more) for the mascarpone, it cuts down on the sugar, and it uses low-fat cocoa powder in place of grated whole chocolate. Just *try* it — then you'll know that I'm not just flapping my gums when I insist that Slim Cuisine is *no compromise!*

15-16 Italian sponge fingers (Savoiardi)	*¾ lb/350 g low- or medium-fat ricotta cheese*
5 fl oz/150 ml strong black coffee	*¾ lb/350 g quark*
1½ teaspoons natural vanilla essence	*3-4 tablespoons granulated NutraSweet*
1 tablespoon Amaretto di Saronno or dark rum	*1 heaped tablespoon low-fat, unsweetened cocoa (see Mail Order Guide page 153)*
1 tablespoon brandy	*½ tablespoon icing sugar*

1 Line the bottom of a shallow rectangular (12 × 7 inch/30.5 × 18 cm) or oval baking dish with one layer of sponge fingers. (You may have to break a few in half.) Stir together the coffee, ½ teaspoon of vanilla essence, Amaretto di Saronno or rum, and brandy. A tablespoon at a time, sprinkle this mixture over the sponge fingers.
2 Combine the ricotta cheese, quark, NutraSweet and remaining vanilla essence in the food processor. Process until smooth and fluffy. Spread this mixture over the sponge fingers.
3 Combine the cocoa and icing sugar. Sift it evenly over the surface of the pudding. Cover the dish and chill.

Note: In this Tiramisu, and the following variation, water processed, decaffeinated filter coffee can be substituted for the strong coffee with absolutely no loss of quality. Also, if you are planning to serve Tiramisu to children, the liqueurs can be eliminated.

 ## CHOCOLATE TIRAMISU

Fills a 12 × 7-inch/30.5 × 18-cm baking dish

Chocolate Tiramisu will gladden the hearts of chocolate connoisseurs everywhere. It tastes so rich and chocolatey, yet the fat levels have been so drastically reduced. Life *does* have its glorious moments.

15-16 Italian sponge fingers (Savoiardi)	medium-fat ricotta cheese and quark
5 fl oz/150 ml strong black coffee	6 tablespoons icing sugar
1½ teaspoons natural vanilla essence	2 tablespoons low-fat, unsweetened cocoa (see Mail
1 tablespoon Amaretto di Saronno	Order Guide, page 153)
1 tablespoon dark rum	1 additional heaped tablespoon low-fat unsweetened cocoa
¾ lb/350 g each low- or	½ tablespoon icing sugar

1   Line the bottom of a shallow rectangular (12 × 7-inch/30.5 × 18-cm) or oval baking dish with one layer of sponge fingers. (You may have to break a few in half.) Stir together the coffee, ½ teaspoon of vanilla essence, Amaretto di Saronno and rum. A tablespoon at a time, sprinkle this mixture over the sponge fingers.

2   Combine the ricotta, quark, 6 tablespoons icing sugar, 2 tablespoons cocoa and remaining vanilla essence in the food processor. Process until smooth and fluffy. Spread this mixture smoothly over the sponge fingers.

3   Sift together the remaining cocoa and icing sugar. Sprinkle it evenly over the surface of the pudding. Cover the dish and chill.

FRUIT-RICOTTA EXTRAVAGANZA

Fills a 12 × 7-inch/30.5 × 18-cm baking dish

This was developed one night in response to my husband's traditional and plaintive query: 'What's for pud?' Inspired by the array of seasonal fruit in my fridge, and the memory of the glorious lower-fat Tiramisu I had developed a few days before, I added a layer of berries and peaches and a topping of crushed Amaretti biscuits in place of the cocoa powder. It was such a rousing success that I made it again for my helpers a few days later. 'What shall I call this fruit-ricotta extravaganza?' I asked them as we all scraped our plates clean in paroxysms of delight. 'Fruit-Ricotta Extravaganza', was the immediate answer.

15-16 Italian sponge fingers (Savoiardi)	2 tablespoons fresh orange juice
	1 tablespoon orange liqueur
1 punnet each: strawberries, blueberries, raspberries	1 lb 6 oz/625 g medium- or low-fat ricotta cheese

2 ripe peaches	3 tablespoons icing sugar
1 teaspoon natural vanilla essence	2 pairs Amaretti biscuits

1   Line the bottom of a shallow, rectangular (12 × 7-inch/30.5 × 18-cm) or oval, clear-glass baking dish with a layer of sponge fingers (you may have to break a few in half).
2   Halve or quarter the strawberries. Combine all the berries in a bowl. Halve and stone the peaches, and cut them into cubes. Add to the berries. Sprinkle on half the vanilla essence and all the orange juice and liqueur and gently toss with two spoons to combine thoroughly. Spread this fruit mixture and juices all over the sponge fingers.
3   Put the ricotta cheese into a food processor with the remaining vanilla essence and the icing sugar. Process until smooth and fluffy and perfectly amalgamated.
4   With a rubber spatula, smooth and spread the cheese mixture over the fruit. As you spread, some of the fruit pieces may partially show through the cheese layer; that's fine.
5   With a kitchen mallet, crush the Amaretti biscuits and sprinkle the crumbs evenly over the cheese layer. Refrigerate for at least two hours.

Note: **Sponge Fingers**
Sponge fingers are *low*-fat, but not *no*-fat: they are made with whole eggs. If you must (or you cook for someone who must) avoid cholesterol altogether, do not use the sponge fingers — bake the flat white sponge cake from the Cassata recipe (see below) instead, and cut it into fingers. Use these fat-free sponge fingers as the base for your Tiramisu.

CASSATA SICILIANA

Makes 1 cake

A low-fat Cassata? Is such a thing possible? And can it possibly taste good? Well, why not? Of course it is! Would I bother with it if it didn't? A cassata is a festive and spectacular three-layered cake constructed from three sponge layers. (Sponge cake is called 'pan di spagna' [Spanish bread] in Italy, although the French call it 'Genoise' [Genoa style]. Go figure it out!) The sponge layers are brushed with liqueur, filled with a sweet ricotta-double cream mixture, and the whole thing is iced with an extremely rich chocolate-butter cream. I wouldn't even tell you about such a dangerously seductive high-fat dessert, if I didn't have a perfectly gorgeous Slim Cuisine clone for you to try; it would be too cruel.

Cake
Makes one sheet cake

2 oz/50 g self-raising sponge flour	Pinch of cream of tartar
1½ oz/40 g caster sugar	2 oz/50 g caster sugar
5 egg whites, at room temperature	1 teaspoon natural vanilla essence

1 Preheat the oven to 350°F, 180°C, Gas Mark 4.
2 Sift together the flour and the 1½ oz/40 g sugar. Set aside.
3 Beat the egg whites until foamy. Add the cream of tartar and beat until they hold soft peaks. Continue beating, adding the remaining 2 oz/50 g sugar, 2 tablespoons at a time, until the sugar is dissolved and the whites are stiff and glossy. Fold in the vanilla essence.
4 A little at a time, sprinkle the sifted flour/sugar mixture over the egg whites and fold in gently but thoroughly.
5 Spread the mixture on to a silicone-paper-lined Swiss roll tin.
6 Bake in the oven for 15-18 minutes.
7 Allow to cool in the pan, on a rack, before peeling the paper off the Swiss roll. Spread a tea towel on your work surface, and turn the cake out on to it.

Filling
Chocolate-Ricotta Cream (page 148) or
Orange-Ricotta Cream (page 147)

❋ Mocha Icing

Makes 2 pts/1.1 l

9 tablespoons low-fat, unsweetened cocoa (see Mail Order Guide, page 153)	8 tablespoons caster sugar
3 tablespoons cornflour	½ teaspoon natural vanilla essence
5 tablespoons skimmed milk powder	12 fl oz/350 ml skimmed milk
	6 fl oz/175 ml cooled coffee

144

1 Sift the cocoa, cornflour, milk powder and sugar into a 3½ pt/2 l, 7-inch/18-cm top diameter, opaque white plastic measuring jug.
2 With a wire whisk, mix the vanilla, milk and coffee into the dry ingredients. Whisk well − you don't want lumps. Cover the jug with cling film.
3 Microwave on full power for 3 minutes. Uncover (begin with the side *away* from you, to release the steam. Be careful − the steam will be hot) and whisk thoroughly. Re-cover and microwave on full power for 2 minutes more. Uncover and whisk again. If the mixture hasn't boiled and thickened by now, microwave for another minute, then whisk again. If necessary, microwave for another ½-1 minute until it is beautifully thickened. Uncover, whisk and let stand for 5 minutes, whisking occasionally. Store with a covering of cling film right on the surface of the icing.

Assembly

¼ pt/150 ml orange liqueur or
   Amaretto di Saronno

1 Cut the cake into thirds. With a pastry brush, brush the top of each third with orange liqueur or Amaretto di Saronno.
2 Line a 2 lb/900 g, 9 × 4½ × 3-inches/23 × 11 × 7.5-cm loaf pan with baking paper. Put one third of cake − liqueur side up − in the pan. Spread with half the flavoured ricotta cream. Top with second third of cake, liqueur side up. Top with the remaining ricotta. Top with last third of cake, liqueur side down. Cover and refrigerate for at least 1 hour. (It can stay in the fridge overnight, if necessary.)
3 Flip over to unmould. With a palette knife, lavish the Mocha Icing on the top and sides. Store in the fridge. Allow to sit at room temperature for an hour before serving in slices.

 CHOCOLATE CASSATA

Makes 1 cake

Use a chocolate batter for the sponge cake instead of a vanilla one to make a chocolate cassata. The filling can be either Vanilla-Ricotta Cream or Chocolate-Ricotta Cream (page 148). Ice with the Mocha Icing (preceding recipe) or a pure chocolate one (recipe follows).

Chocolate Cake

Makes 1 sheet cake

1½ oz/40 g self-raising sponge flour	5 egg whites, at room temperature
3 tablespoons low-fat, unsweetened cocoa (see Mail Order Guide, page 153)	Pinch of cream of tartar
	2 oz/50 g caster sugar
1½ oz/40 g caster sugar	1 teaspoon natural vanilla essence

1 Preheat the oven to 350°F, 180°C, Gas Mark 4.
2 Sift together the flour, cocoa, and the 1½ oz/40 g sugar. Set aside.
3 Beat the egg whites until foamy. Add the cream of tartar and beat until they hold soft peaks. Continue beating, adding the remaining 2 oz/50 g sugar, 2 tablespoons at a time, until the sugar is dissolved and the whites are stiff and glossy. Fold in the vanilla essence.
4 A little at a time, sprinkle the sifted flour, cocoa, sugar mixture over the egg whites and fold in gently but thoroughly.
5 Spread the mixture on to a silicone-paper-lined Swiss roll tin.
6 Bake in the oven for 15-18 minutes.
7 Allow to cool on a rack before peeling the paper off the Swiss roll.

✳ Chocolate Icing

Makes 2 pts/1.1 l

9 tablespoons low-fat, unsweetened cocoa (see Mail Order Guide, page 153)	8 tablespoons caster sugar
	½ teaspoon natural vanilla essence
3 tablespoons cornflour	
5 tablespoons skimmed milk powder	Approximately 18 fl oz/500 ml skimmed milk (1 longlife carton)

1 Sift the cocoa, cornflour, milk powder and sugar into a 3½ pt/2 l, 7-inch/18-cm top diameter, opaque white plastic measuring jug.
2 With a wire whisk, mix the vanilla and milk into the dry ingredients. Whisk well − you don't want lumps. Cover the jug with cling film.

3   Microwave on full power for 3 minutes. Uncover (begin with the side *away* from you to release the steam. Be careful — the steam will be hot) and whisk thoroughly. Re-cover and microwave on full power for 2 minutes more. Uncover and whisk again. If the mixture hasn't boiled and thickened by now, microwave for another minute, then whisk again. If necessary, microwave for another ½-1 minute until it is beautifully thickened. Uncover, whisk and let stand for 5 minutes, whisking occasionally. Store with a covering of cling film right on the surface of the mixture.

4   Assemble as for the Cassata Siciliana on page 145.

Note: After trimming and cutting the sheet cake and building a cassata, you may have some cake, some ricotta filling and some icing left. Use these wonderful bits and pieces to build a coffee cup pudding. Cut the leftover cake into little strips and use them to line the bottom and sides of a small, elegant coffee cup. Spread on some of the chocolate icing and top with the ricotta mixture. Sprinkle some cocoa powder and icing sugar over the top. Chill.

 ## ORANGE-RICOTTA CREAM

Makes ¾ pt/400 ml

Serve this creamy, orange-scented, mousse-like ricotta pudding on its own, as a garnish to other recipes (such as Stuffed Peaches or Pears) or as a Cassata filling.

1 lb/450 g low- or medium-fat ricotta cheese	(to taste)
1 heaped tablespoon orange marmalade	1 teaspoon natural vanilla essence
Approximately 3 tablespoons granulated NutraSweet	1 tablespoon orange liqueur (Grand Marnier or Cointreau)

1   Combine all the ingredients in a food processor container. Process until well mixed and fluffy. Taste and add a bit more sweetener if you think it's needed.

2   Pipe or spoon the mixture into dessert goblets and chill until serving time.

Variation:

 ## VANILLA-RICOTTA CREAM

Makes ¾ pt/400 ml

As above, but omit the marmalade and the orange liqueur.

 ## CHOCOLATE-RICOTTA CREAM

Makes 1 pt/570 ml

Chocolate lovers everywhere: are you listening? This tastes like the most wickedly indulgent chocolate mousse in the world. It's the 2 egg whites, beaten to firm peaks and folded into the ricotta, that helps give this irresistible pud its richness. Egg whites are virtually fat-free, but – to avoid salmonella – you must buy them from a trusted supplier, *never* use a cracked egg, and be meticulous about storing eggs in the refrigerator. And it is best to never serve a raw egg-white dessert to the very young, or the elderly.

1 lb/450 g low-fat ricotta cheese	*1 teaspoon natural vanilla*
3 tablespoons icing sugar	*essence*
1 tablespoon low-fat,	*2 teaspoons dark rum*
unsweetened cocoa (see Mail	*2 egg whites*
Order Guide, page 153)	*Pinch cream of tartar*

1   Put the ricotta, 1 tablespoon sugar, the cocoa, vanilla essence and rum into a food processor and process until perfectly smooth and combined. Scrape into a large bowl.
2   Beat the egg whites with a wire whisk or electric beater. When they are foaming, add the cream of tartar. Beat in the remaining sugar, a little at a time, until the whites hold firm peaks and are glossy.
3   Stir ¼ of the egg whites into the ricotta mixture to lighten it. Fold in the remainder with a rubber spatula, using an over-under motion, and turning the bowl as you fold. Spoon or pipe the mixture into dessert goblets and chill.

DEEP CHOCOLATE SORBET

Makes 1 pt/570 ml

When I think about Rome, I think about the Piazza Navona, a table outside Tre Scalini, and *Tartuffo*, that dark (almost black), sexy, luscious, concoction of chocolate ice cream and cherries. Tre Scalini's Tartuffo is almost indecent in its pure, deep chocolate directness; it's hard to even think about it without becoming just slightly short of breath. After I've contemplated the memory of the sublime Tartuffo, I may spare a few thoughts for the Bernini Fountain on the Piazza; for the ceiling of the Sistine Chapel, for the Colosseum, but my thoughts keep coming back to that chocolate enchantment. Deep Chocolate Sorbet (first published in *Slim Cuisine: Indulgent Desserts*) was my attempt to capture a low-fat version of that deep dark magic. The first time I served it to a particularly good chocolate-loving friend, she took the first mouthful and then gasped. I could see that *look* on her face: that slowly dawning astonishment at the totally over-the-top chocolatiness of the experience. 'It's sex on a plate!' she gasped. And she was quite right, too. Serve scoops of the sorbet with Cherry Compôte and its juices (page 133) nestled on the side. If fresh cherries are not available, raspberries will do nicely. Dare I say that this manages to *surpass* the original Tartuffo experience? Perhaps you'd better try it and decide for yourself.

8 oz/225 g caster sugar	page 153)
18 fl oz/475 ml water	½ teaspoon natural vanilla
2 oz/50 g low-fat, unsweetened	essence
cocoa (see Mail Order Guide,	

1 Combine the sugar and water in a saucepan and heat gently until the sugar has dissolved. Raise the heat and boil for 1 minute. Remove from the heat and allow to cool a bit.
2 Stir a little of the sugar-water syrup into the cocoa in a bowl and make a smooth paste, then gradually stir in the remaining syrup.
3 Add the vanilla essence. Strain the mixture through a fine sieve. Cool thoroughly.
4 Freeze in an ice cream maker, following the manufacturer's instructions. Serve on *cold* plates (it melts quickly).

'He then took me to the glorious Piazza Navona, where
we strolled past three of the most beautiful fountain

statues I'd ever seen. He kept repeating, "Bernini, Bernini". We sat at a midnight cafe and had luscious ice cream, which I assumed was called bernini. He didn't stop kissing me, but all the strolling couples were so busy necking, no one noticed. There's nothing quite as delicious as berninis and kisses. At one point I didn't know who was eating which ice cream. I guess that's what they mean by chocolate-covered kisses.'

Shelley Winters, *Shelley*

 # POLENTA FRUITCAKE

Makes one 8-inch/20.5-cm cake

I first read about Polenta Fruitcake in Marcella Hazan's second book, *More Classic Italian Cooking.* It was an idea that took beautifully to drastic fat reduction. What a marvellous Christmas treat it would make: the cake overflows with dried fruit and the haunting anise taste of fennel seeds. Sometimes I serve it with Spiced Red Vermouth Syrup (page 140).

¾ pt/400 ml water	*5 oz/150 g ready-to-eat dried*
2 pinches salt	*figs, diced*
6 oz/175 g quick cooking polenta	*3 egg whites, lightly beaten*
5 oz/150 g caster sugar	*1-1½ tablespoons fennel seeds*
1 oz/25 g pine nuts	*5 oz/150 g sifted self-raising*
2½ oz/60 g sultanas	*flour*

1 Preheat the oven to 400°F, 200°C, Gas Mark 6.
2 Bring the water to just below the boil in a saucepan. Add the salt and pour in the polenta in a slow, even stream while stirring thoroughly with a whisk. Switch to a wooden spoon and stir and cook until smooth and thick and the mixture pulls away from the sides of the pan.
3 Stir the sugar, pine nuts, sultanas, figs, egg whites and fennel seeds into the cooked polenta. Mix them together very well. Add the flour and beat until the mixture is well amalgamated.
4 Spoon and scrape the batter into an 8-inch/20.5-cm diameter, 2-inch/5-cm deep, non-stick, removable-bottom cake tin. Bake for approximately 30-35 minutes. (The top will be dry and slightly crackled, and a cake tester will test clean.) When done, loosen all around with a palette knife, and remove the sides. Cool on a rack.

Pizza – rustic, simple and irresistibly delicious: from right to left:
pizza with tomato sauce, mozzarella, grilled peppers, Parma ham,
olives and basil; potato pizza.

Sublime endings: anticlockwise from the foreground: deep chocolate sorbet with raspberries; tiramisu; peach-Amaretti mess.

STRAWBERRY ICE

Makes 1 pt/570 ml

This strawberry ice, quickly made in a food processor from frozen strawberries and citrus juice ice cubes, is like an Italian Granita: icy, vivid with the taste of its enforming berry, and very refreshing on a hot day.

5 fl oz/150 ml orange juice	8 oz/225 g frozen strawberries
1 fl oz/25 ml lemon juice	A little extra lemon juice
Grated zest of ¼ of each fruit	NutraSweet to taste

1   Combine the juices and rind and freeze in ice cube trays.
2   Put the frozen strawberries in a food processor. Process until splintery. (If the machine jams, turn it off, free the blade, and continue.)
3   While the machine is running, drop the fruit juice cubes, one by one, into the machine, and sprinkle a tablespoon or two of NutraSweet through the tube. Add a few drops of lemon juice. Stop the machine and taste the mixture. Add more sweetener if needed, but remember: this ice should be tart. Process for a minute or two more until the mixture forms an icy sorbet. Serve at once.

Mail Order Guide

Write or telephone for a price
list.

Anton's Delicatessen 101 Hare Lane Claygate Esher Surrey KT10 0QX Tel: 0372 462306	Balsamic vinegar Dry-pack sun-dried tomatoes Quick-cooking polenta Dried mushrooms
Culpeper Limited Hadstock Road Linton Cambridgeshire CB1 6NJ Tel: 0223 894054	Californian dry-pack sun-dried tomatoes, no added salt
Italian Taste 32 Abbeygate Street Bury St Edmunds Suffolk Tel: 0284 752605	Dry-pack sun-dried tomatoes Balsamic vinegar Quick-cooking polenta Dried mushrooms

Health Craze
Cromwell Court
115 Earls Court Road
London
SW5

Tel: 071-244 7784

Parson's Trading Limited
PO Box 995
Purton
Swindon
Wiltshire
SN5 9WB

Tel: 0793 772200

Cambridge Continental Store
9 The Broadway
Mill Road
Cambridge
CB1 3AH

Tel: 0223 248069

Stock powders
Balsamic vinegar
Dry-pack sun-dried tomatoes
Quick-cooking polenta

Low-fat, unsweetened cocoa
    powder

Balsamic vinegar
Dry-pack sun-dried tomatoes
Quick-cooking polenta
Dried mushrooms

Index

157

159

160